D1288483

A THOUSAND GEESE

Books by Peter Scott

- MORNING FLIGHT
- WILD CHORUS
- THE BATTLE OF THE NARROW SEAS
- PORTRAIT DRAWINGS
- WILD GEESE AND ESKIMOS

Books by James Fisher

- BIRDS AS ANIMALS
- THE BIRDS OF BRITAIN
- BIRDS OF THE VILLAGE
- BIRDS OF THE FIELD
- BIRD RECOGNITION (*to be of four volumes*)
- THE FULMAR
- WATCHING BIRDS
- SEA-BIRDS (*with R. M. Lockley*)

Goslings and moulted adult Pinkfeet rounded up for ringing on the crest of Arnafellsalda in Central Iceland

PETER SCOTT AND
JAMES FISHER

A THOUSAND GEESE

COLLINS
ST JAMES'S PLACE LONDON
1953

For

FINNUR GUÐMUNDSSON

may his shadow never grow less

Printed in Great Britain
Collins Clear-Type Press: London and Glasgow

Contents

Contents

Appendices

Illustrations

FRONTISPIECE

IN BLACK AND WHITE

MAPS

CHAPTER I

Introduction

A QUARTER OF A CENTURY AGO the middle reaches of the river Nene in Northamptonshire—which wind through a noble limestone landscape with green pasture fields, small old villages and medieval churches—were regularly flooded every winter. During the Second World War the agriculture of these reaches was " improved " by dredgers and excavators. The River Nene was gouged and scoured ; and the waters now no longer spread over the meadows but rush straight down to the Wash. Now the water-meadows must, we suppose, be called—just meadows ; and perhaps they now carry more stock than they did. But, with the disappearance of the floods, something else has dropped out of the landscape—the wildfowl ; and particularly the wild geese. No longer do goose-flocks come to this inland English refuge from the tundras of western Siberia or the Arctic islands.

If you visit the Titchmarsh water-meadows nowadays in late winter, you will see plenty of birds. The herons will be rattling about in the heronry in the duck decoy, as they have for years, and there will be packs of duck on the river, mostly mallard and teal, some wigeon. But never thousands, and never geese. Yet when the writers of this book were schoolboys and sometimes watched the Titchmarsh waterfowl together, they could log all three species of swans, four kinds of geese and fourteen kinds of duck. Though they did not know it at the time, many expeditions, including the one which is the subject of this book, started with those goose-watching days of the nineteen-twenties.

In the minds of boys in their early teens, interest, even obsession, can be fixed, given the right circumstances and ceremonies, and the right master of them. The writers were led enthusiastically to bird-watching in general and goose-watching in particular by Kenneth Fisher, headmaster of one and father of the other: an enthusiast from whom we learned what we know of the discipline of orderly note-taking, of the futility of aimless nature-watching, of the necessity of knowing what you are after and why, while at the same time remaining receptive to any surprise or opportunity that may turn up. Since those days, neither of us has learned as much about birds or bird-watching as he has had opportunity for. But neither has lacked opportunity to pursue his obsession, each in his somewhat different way. This introductory chapter was, for instance, drafted by the second author, since (the rest of the book having been finished) the first author was flown on another wild-goose chase, this time to Tierra del Fuego, taking Phil, his wife, with him. When Peter and Philippa Scott return from what is almost the sub-Antarctic, no doubt with many scientific observations, films and records, and perhaps even new geese or ducks for the Severn Wildfowl Trust collection, they will find James Fisher flown to indulge his main obsession, sea-birds—to study those of Newfoundland, New England, Florida, Texas, California, Alaska and the Seal Islands.

But whatever the fortunes of our latest expeditions, we shall always remember Iceland, 1951, as the expedition that could not go wrong; where nature and man conspired to help us all the time. It was almost uncanny how everything fell into place.

The mystery of the world's pinkfoot population had occupied the literature for some years. It was obvious that there was one big secret to be unlocked, the secret of this species' main breeding grounds. For some time Peter Scott's winter researches with his fellow-members of the Severn Wildfowl Trust, and with a new technique for catching geese, had guided his attention to this unsolved problem. Congreve and Freme, exploring Iceland in 1929, found the first clue. Icelandic investigators, the latest of them Finnur Guðmundsson, found further clues. By 1950 a journey to the heart of Iceland became the expedition that *had* to be made, the problem that naturally posed itself.

Very few of the major discoveries about birds in general, or about wild geese in particular, have been the result of a special and deliberate campaign. Apart from the grey lag, our detailed knowledge of the wild geese of Britain has been practically all gained in the last hundred years, and most of it in the twentieth century. As we shall see, the breeding grounds of the pinkfoot, the hero of this story, were not discovered in Spitsbergen till 1855, in Greenland till 1891 and in Iceland till 1929. Except for the last discovery, these were all results of expeditions in which goose-hunting was not the primary objective. The same goes for the breeding grounds of the barnacle goose, the last northern goose except one to disclose its nest to the ornithological world. It was E. Bay, the man who first discovered the pinkfoot nesting in Greenland, who also discovered the barnacle to be a breeding bird in Scoresby Sound in 1891. Although the barnacle had been recognised in Spitsbergen and had been suspected to breed there since 1858, its restricted nesting grounds were not actually found till 1907, by the Koenig expedition.

The last wild goose of the north to have its breeding grounds discovered was the little Ross's goose, *Anser rossii*, whose nesting colonies were found for the first time in 1938 in the Perry River area of Arctic Canada by Angus Gavin. In 1949 one of us made what must have been one of the first expeditions primarily devoted to a single species of goose. The Perry River expedition of 1949, described in Peter Scott's *Wild Geese and Eskimos*, was sponsored by the Arctic Institute of North America, with additional support from *Life* magazine, Ducks Unlimited and Colonel Arthur Sullivan of Winnipeg. The objects of the expedition were to find and map the interesting breeding range of this little goose, to mark as many as possible, to estimate the breeding population and to bring some living specimens back to the collection of the Severn Wildfowl Trust in England.

All these objects were achieved and the geese which were brought back now breed each year in Gloucestershire.

Ross's goose, which is believed to have a world population of about 3,000 individuals, cannot possibly be described as an abundant or dominant species, though it is extraordinarily interesting. But the pinkfoot is the most abundant wild grey goose of Britain, and has a population which, as we shall see, is usually between 30,000 and 50,000 individuals. Yet, considering its abundance and familiarity, its breeding grounds in 1951 were almost as little known as were those of Ross's goose in 1949.

The pinkfoot expedition of 1951 would, like the expedition to the Perry River in 1949, have been impossible without substantial financial support. The modernisation of equipment and ease of most communication has not materially reduced the cost of exploring; in any case, the Severn Wildfowl Trust Expedition to the Hofsjökull could rely on nothing more modern than horses. It was interesting to find how unanimously this ancient and traditional means of transport proved to be effective, and to the taste of the members of the expedition. Half the cost of the expedition was borne by the Royal Society, and this we most gratefully acknowledge. The Icelandic Government, through its Natural History Museum, paid for a quarter of it; and apart from this important contribution, gave much help in other ways, and certain privileges. The rest of the cost of the expedition came from grants from the Severn Wildfowl Trust and the *Geographical Magazine*, from the publication of articles in *The Times* and the *Manchester Guardian*, and from broadcast talks.

There are many others who were generous with time and trouble to help the expedition. Among our kind friends we would, particularly, like to thank Jack Greenway, the British Minister in Iceland. The Ministers Residence, near the shore on the north side of Reykjavík, was a second home to us both before and after the expedition. The English three-quarters of the expedition would also like to thank the charming wife of Finnur Guðmundsson, the Icelandic quarter. Guðríður Gísladóttir was kind and hospitable, and looked after many complicated arrangements, not least of which was the deciphering of the somewhat garbled wireless messages that we managed to get through. One of the two Icelandic Airlines, Flugfélag Íslands, arranged the famous air-drop of stores described on page 165. We thank them not only for their flight but also for the accuracy of their bomb-aiming. Many kind friends and correspondents in Britain helped the expedition with the identification of some of the specimens it brought home, particularly Miss Cynthia Longfield, Dr. E. B. Ford, F.R.S., Professor H. Munro Fox, F.R.S., S. Prudhoe, J. P. Harding, D. E. Kimmins and T. H. Savory.

With the survey of the literature of the pinkfoot made by the second author for this book and for the scientific paper in the *Fifth Annual Report of the Severn Wildfowl Trust* (Scott, Fisher and Guðmundsson, 1953) we must particularly thank the following for help: with translation from Icelandic, Dr. H. G. Vevers; from Icelandic and Danish, Guðríður Gísladóttir; from Danish, Norwegian and Swedish, S. T. England; from German, Dr. S. F. Winter; from Latin, Miss J. W. Fisher.

Hugh Boyd, resident biologist to the Severn Wildfowl Trust,

has been most helpful over statistical work on population problems, particularly in Appendix E.

To our patient, cheerful and skilful guides we owe a great debt. They were the Icelandic farmers Jóhann Sigurðsson, Snjólfur Snjólfsson, Ágúst Sveinsson and Valentínus Jónsson. Valentínus Jónsson (Valli), who stayed with us for most of the time that we spent in the central oasis under the Hofsjökull, was wise, energetic and enterprising. The expedition would have had little success without him (and his fine horse).

But most of all, we would like to thank the man to whom this book is affectionately dedicated, the Director of Iceland's National Museum, Dr. Finnur Guðmundsson. On him fell practically all the task of the preliminary arrangements in Iceland for the expedition. We know how difficult it is to make arrangements with farmers for the use of their time and horses in the summer months when farm work is at its height. That we were able to enlist some of the best farmers in South Iceland is a great credit to Finnur's skill in negotiation. Finnur has had wide personal experience of inland travel in Iceland. Like most Icelanders, he was born and brought up on a farm, and his knowledge of the great island must be almost, if not quite, unique. In search of Iceland's birds he has for many years spent the summer in the field in some remote part of his own wonderful country, ranging from Grímsey in the north to his wife's family's farmstead at Vík in the south, from Langanes in the east to Snæfellsnes and the North-West Peninsula. He has penetrated into the interior up many of the great rivers, that rush down from the central plateau, from the ice-caps and snows, through deep basalt gorges and over steep and sudden falls. Everywhere he has made methodical bird notes, and established contact with local farmers, among whom amateur nature-watching has always been a hobby and who are very reliable observers. He has been for many years revising and improving the national bird collection and accumulating material and evidence for a new *Birds of Iceland*, which will one day be the standard work on the subject, another step forward in the already noble tradition of Icelandic bird-recording, which dates from the visits of the great Friedrich Faber (1822) in 1820, and which includes such notable names as Alfred Newton (1863), Berhnhard Hantzsch (1905) and Bjarni Sæmundsson (1936). Not only is Finnur a very able scientist; he was a most amiable and amusing companion on our expedition.

Practically everybody who has been on an expedition comes back with theories as to the optimum numbers a party should consist of. Judging from our own experience in several expeditions, we agree that there is no such thing as a perfect number, and there is no intrinsic difference in the compatibility of two, three, four or five members. There was never a time in the whole of our stay at our central camp when we felt that our expedition was too big, and we only felt it was too small on occasions when one of us was out of action or when we lacked fielders in the complicated tactical games that we played to catch the geese.

We must pay two more tokens of respect. One is to Phil. Even in these days some people think there is no place for a woman on a long field expedition. Phil was a better rider than the other English members of the expedition; could stand a fifteen-hour walk almost without turning a hair; and could catch, and hold still to be ringed, a couple of hundred frisky netted geese and goslings without incurring anything more serious than a good appetite. She made our mess-tent more like a home than a camp. In fact, she did a man's share of the work, and a woman's share on top of it.

The other is to the wonderful country of the pinkfeet—Iceland, with its historical and natural treasures—Iceland, on the edge of nowhere, populated by not many more than a hundred thousand proud people. How can so small a population, living in a difficult environment, support a language, a university, a literature, art, science, theatre of its own?

Of course, Iceland has been through long periods of darkness since the Colonisation over a thousand years ago, and its latest renaissance is a comparatively new one. But we have begun to understand, from our visits to different parts of this strange, often grim, always unexpectedly colourful land, how it is that the Icelanders (who could succeed in any part of the world) have stayed to accept, meet and enjoy the challenge of fire, ice and sea: the red, white and blue of their young national flag.

CHAPTER II

First Catch Your Goose

JUST BEFORE a calm October sunrise the first wild geese lifted from the sandbanks of a Scottish firth and headed inland towards their feeding grounds. There were twenty geese in the skein; and they flew high over a village, over a railway, over two main roads and three miles of farm lands, before they came to the familiar stubble-fields where they had been feeding each day for nearly a week. They began to glide down and to circle over the oat-stubble. It seemed that they were not, after all, the first geese to leave the firth, for already half a dozen were there ahead of them. They hardly seemed to notice that those half-dozen were strangely still, nor could they have known that underneath the feathers were bodies of wood-wool. So they landed beside the decoys, and stood for a while looking at them. The lack of movement made them feel slightly uncomfortable, but some of their number began to feed. Fifty more geese were already circling over the field, and the distant roar of goose voices indicated that more still were on the way. Above the wood on the hill behind was a great skein of five hundred, and as it reached the familiar fields the long lines of its V-formation broke; the geese came

tumbling down like autumn leaves in a gale. Nearer the ground they re-formed into a tight flock, which swept backwards and forwards in the low orange sunlight over the thick cluster of geese on the ground. At each sweep more geese dropped down on fast-flapping wings, and the crowd on the ground became a solid blue-grey patch on the yellow stubble. Still more skeins were coming over the wood, tumbling down, circling and settling, and the chorus of their calling rose and fell like waves breaking on the shore. More than a thousand were down now, and the original six still ones were swamped and unnoticed by the crowd of moving, feeding, quarrelling, preening geese.

None of them had noticed the little camouflaged box on wheels which stood in the corner of the field close to the hedge. None of them knew that four human beings were sitting inside it, watching through narrow shuttered windows, gauging the exact position of the flock through binoculars which wobbled with excitement. Stuck into the stubble straw were markers—white-tipped goose tail-feathers; and the thickest part of the flock was within the square they formed. Long nets lay folded

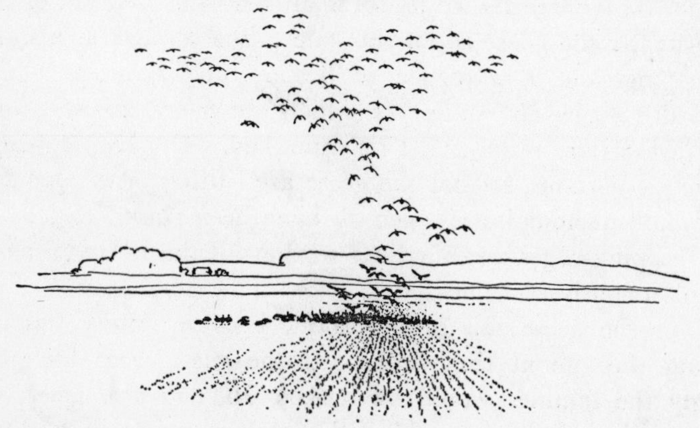

and hidden under a thin layer of straw and grass, the rockets which were to propel them lay in the little holes which had been dug for them, equally well hidden, and connected to the hide by 150 yards of wire flex. For once, after days of preparation and misfortune, everything had gone right for the goose catchers.

The flight had been a fast one, flock following flock before the first ones had had time to disperse across the field. The geese had pitched in the right place, no suspicion of the nets or decoys had caused them to flare, or to swing wide before settling, no untimely shepherd or rabbit-catcher or aeroplane had appeared to disturb them, and now they were feeding right in the catching area—now was the time. "Start the cameras—one, two, three, four, five, FIRE." With a swish the rockets leap out and carry the nets over a part of the flock. It's a catch, a big catch, with more than a hundred geese under the nets.

A jeep drives on to the field, the party from the hide runs out and the marking of the geese begins. As each bird is taken out of the net it is brought to the ringer, who slips a numbered and addressed aluminium ring on to its leg and closes the ring with pliers. The details are written down in a notebook. Then the white tail is dipped into a bucket of dye and finally the goose is put into one of the compartments of a "keeping-cage"—a device of hessian and bamboo which provides a row of "stalls" in which the geese can wait until the last of their number has been marked. The keeping-cages have no bottoms, so that the geese are sitting on the ground, and half an hour later, when all have been ringed and dyed, the keeping-cages are lifted off so that all the birds fly away simultaneously as a flock.

For the geese this is important, because family ties are strong throughout the winter. If the geese were liberated singly the families would be broken up, and also geese are more vulnerable when alone than when flying in a flock. After a catch the released geese form up into a V and fly off towards the estuary.

These rocket nets were invented and developed by the Severn Wildfowl Trust in 1948 (although a comparable method using small cannons to propel the net was developed soon afterwards, and quite independently, in America). During the winter of 1950–51 the Trust's netting team caught and ringed no less than 634 pinkfeet, mostly in Scotland. In subsequent winters we have caught even more.

Apart from the scientific value of the results, the actual netting is immensely exciting. How often we have sat breath-

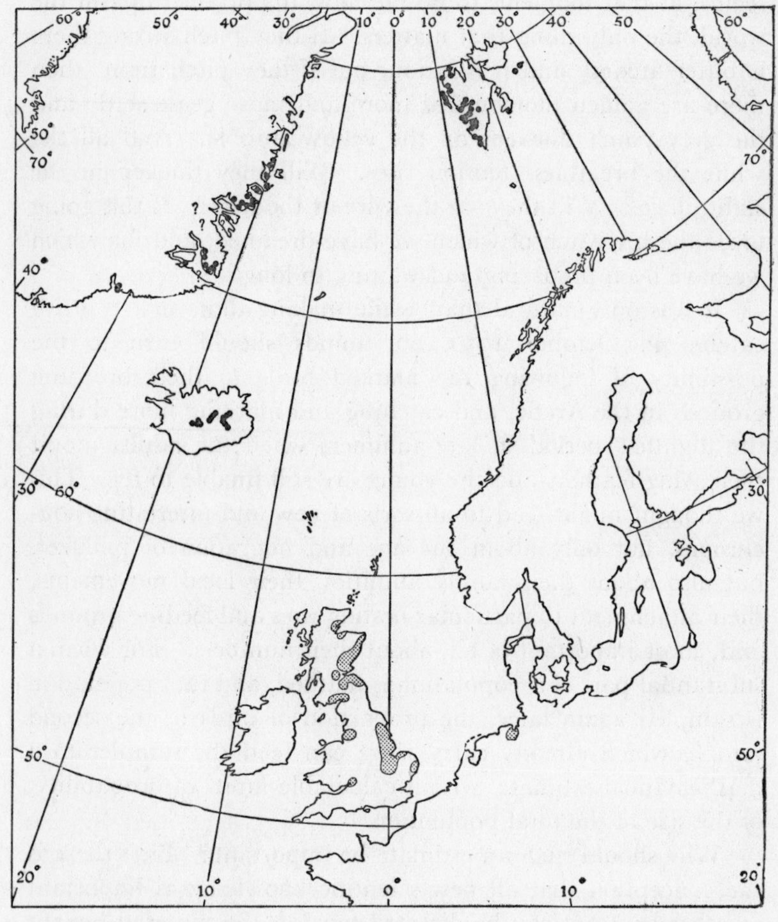

WORLD DISTRIBUTION OF PINKFEET. SUMMER AND WINTER

Dots represent breeding colonies; shaded areas indicate winter feeding-grounds

lessly in the trailer-hide as the first geese prepared to settle. The precise point at which the first bird puts down its feet seems, at that moment, to be the most important thing in the world, the only thing that matters. If they pitch wrong there is bitter anxiety and frustration, but if they pitch right, then there are golden moments as more and more geese settle and the grey patch thickens on the yellow stubble. And all the while the breathless tension rises. Will they thicken in the right place? Will they see the wire or the nets? Is this going to be the big catch of which we have dreamed, and for which we have been preparing and waiting so long?

It was only natural that, while making those first Scottish catches in October 1950, our minds should turn to the possibility of following the marked birds to their breeding grounds in the Arctic, and catching and marking more during the flightless period in late summer, when the adults moult their wing feathers and the young are still unable to fly. This we thought might lead to all sorts of new and interesting conclusions, not only about the age and migration of pinkfeet, but also about their family affinities, their local movements, their attachment to particular nesting sites and feeding grounds and, most important of all, about their numbers. For when a substantial part of a population is marked, and that population is sampled again later, the proportion of birds in the second sample which already carry rings can lead the sampler to a mathematical estimate, within calculable limits of probability, of the size of the total population.

Why should such an estimate be important? First there is the conception that all new scientific knowledge is important whether or not it can be directed towards the material benefit of mankind. The authors of this book believe passionately in this idea. The study of birds only rarely has significance in the field of economics, but mankind would be the poorer without a capacity to be curious about the living creatures which share his world, and poorer still without the creatures

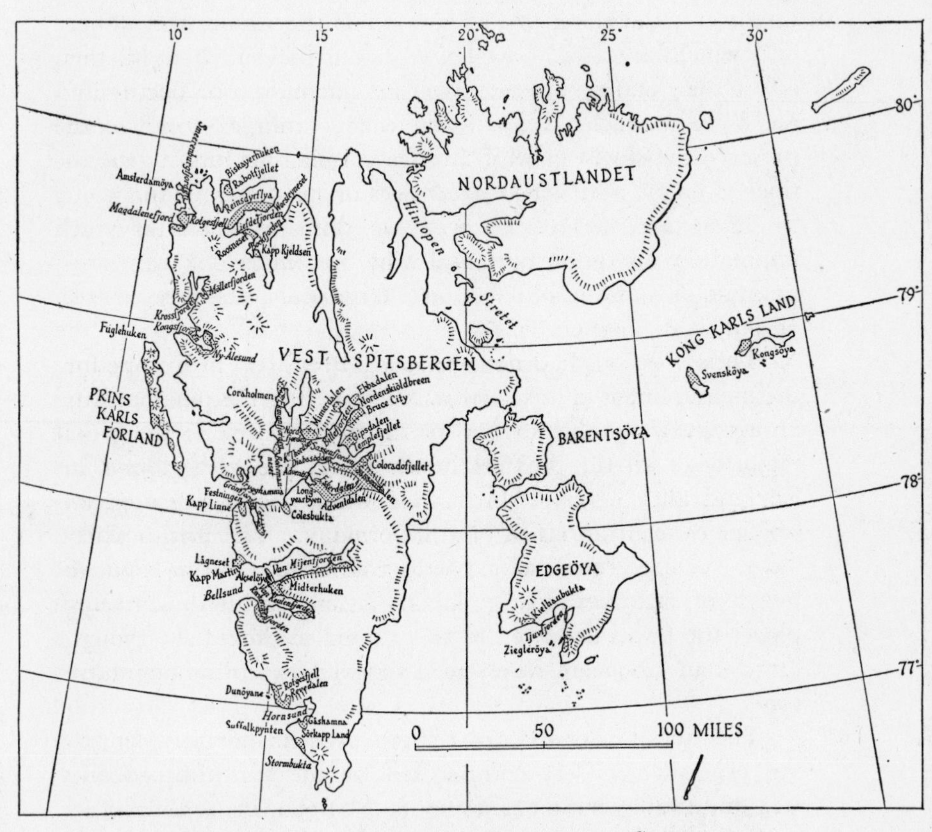

Distribution of breeding Pinkfeet in Spitsbergen

Stippled areas : Coastal and valley tundras carrying a resident summer population

themselves. Yet many species have already been exterminated as a direct result of man's greed and thoughtlessness. Such a danger threatens various kinds of ducks and geese. It is important, therefore, to find out which species are threatened and which are safe, how acute is the danger, what factors affect their status, whether they are increasing or decreasing and by how much. We must know these things before we can preserve the stocks of wild ducks and geese for future generations to enjoy, whether as naturalists or sportsmen or both.

These are the reasons why we think estimates of total population are important and why we undertook this programme of marking pinkfeet on a large scale, which set us off on our wild-goose chase.

These methods had not previously been used in Europe for the measurement of any bird population, and the pinkfoot was an especially suitable species for the project because the great majority of all the pinkfeet in the world are to be found in England and Scotland during the winter, with a few much smaller concentrations in North Germany. The British pinkfeet are centred round some twenty traditional roosting grounds mostly on estuaries or large lakes. At each of these wintering places the flocks are often to be counted in thousands, though more than 5,000 are rarely seen together except at migration time.

The question of following them to their northern breeding headquarters was complicated by the fact that nobody was quite sure whether it lay in Spitsbergen, in Greenland or in Iceland, or whether the population was equally divided between these three recorded nesting grounds.

In the chief island of Spitsbergen, where breeding pinkfeet were first discovered in 1855, their distribution among the arctic poppies and saxifrages of these High Arctic valleys is now well known. Indeed, the information from thirty or forty expeditions to Spitsbergen has made it possible to compile a map which probably marks the parts of the island inhabited

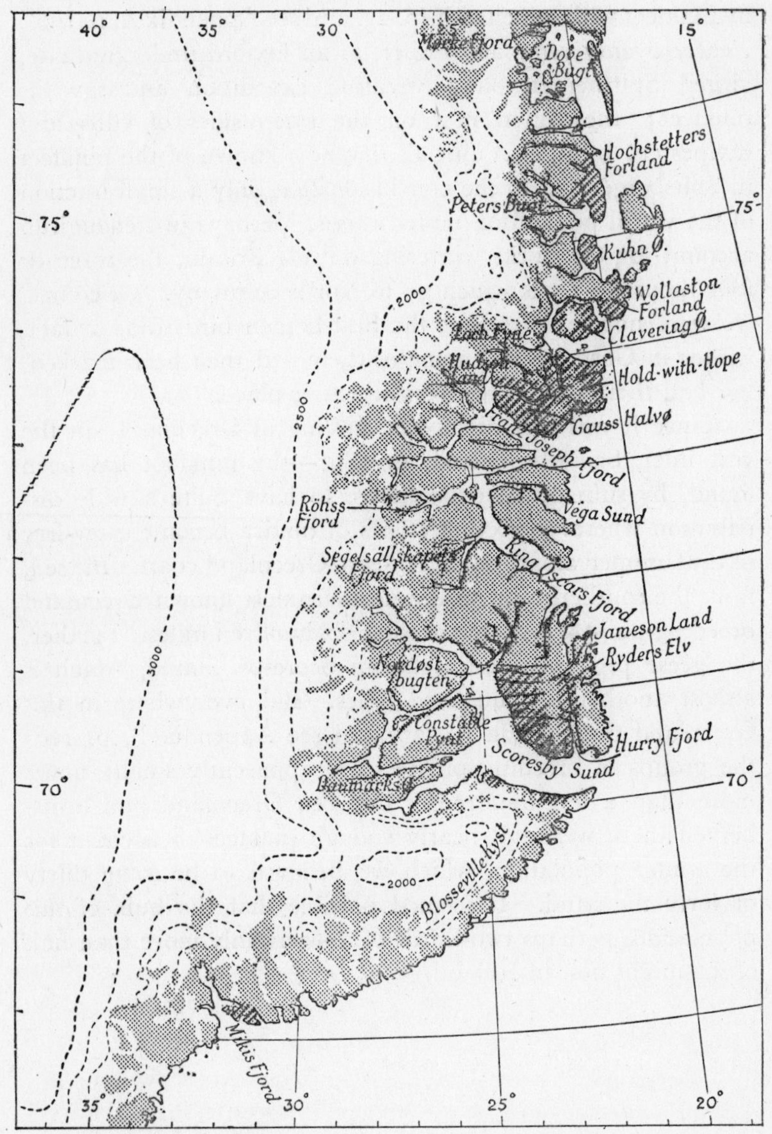

DISTRIBUTION OF BREEDING PINKFEET IN GREENLAND

Marked areas: coastal and valley tundras carrying a resident summer population. Stippled areas: land not under permanent ice

by pinkfeet with some truth (p. 23, and see Appendix A, p. 190). Nearly twenty years ago Fisher, as an Oxford undergraduate, visited Spitsbergen on a vacation expedition and saw its pinkfeet; they often nest on the steep sides of cliffs and ravines cut by rivers. But all that was known of the pinkfeet in Spitsbergen led to the conclusion that only a small fraction of the world population nested there; perhaps just enough to account for the flocks wintering outside Britain, the three or four thousand birds which go to North Germany. Of course, we were not yet sure that the Spitsbergen birds did, in fact, winter in Germany, for none of them had then been marked, nor had there been a recovery in either place.

Since it was first discovered nesting in Greenland—in the vast inlet, Scoresby Sound, in 1891—the pinkfoot has been found, by subsequent expeditions, to have quite a wide distribution wherever good stretches of tundra become snow-free in the summer along the north-east Greenland coast. Indeed, from the southernmost to the northernmost known Greenland breeding-point is a stretch of some six hundred miles. Further, the geese probably nest right up Scoresby Sound, which is almost another two hundred miles. But everywhere in this Greenland distribution (p. 25, and see Appendix B, p. 199) the groups of breeding pinkfeet are apparently small—never more than a few hundreds. Between Greenland and Spitsbergen there were not nearly enough pinkfeet to account for the winter population, which we believed to be some thirty or forty thousand. It seemed possible that the bulk of this population, perhaps two-thirds of it—certainly more than half of it—might nest in Iceland.

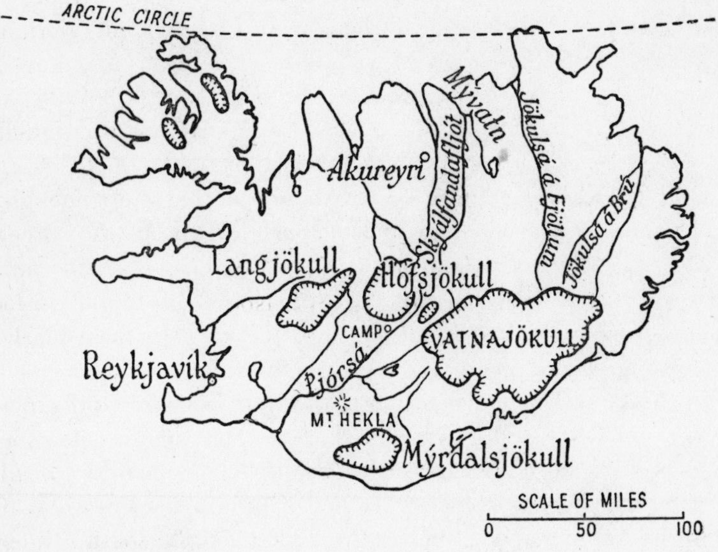

CHAPTER III

The Way In

ICELAND IS AN OVAL-SHAPED country about the size of Ireland; in its present form it is a product of the Tertiary upheavals and what appears to have been more or less continuous volcanic activity ever since. The fertile and cultivable parts of the country are confined to the coastal strip and some sheltered valleys. A very large ice-cap, Vatnajökull (larger than any English county except Yorkshire), occupies over three thousand square miles of the south-east, and three other largish ice-caps occupy the centre and the south. One of these, the Hofsjökull, is a round boss of ice, over twenty miles

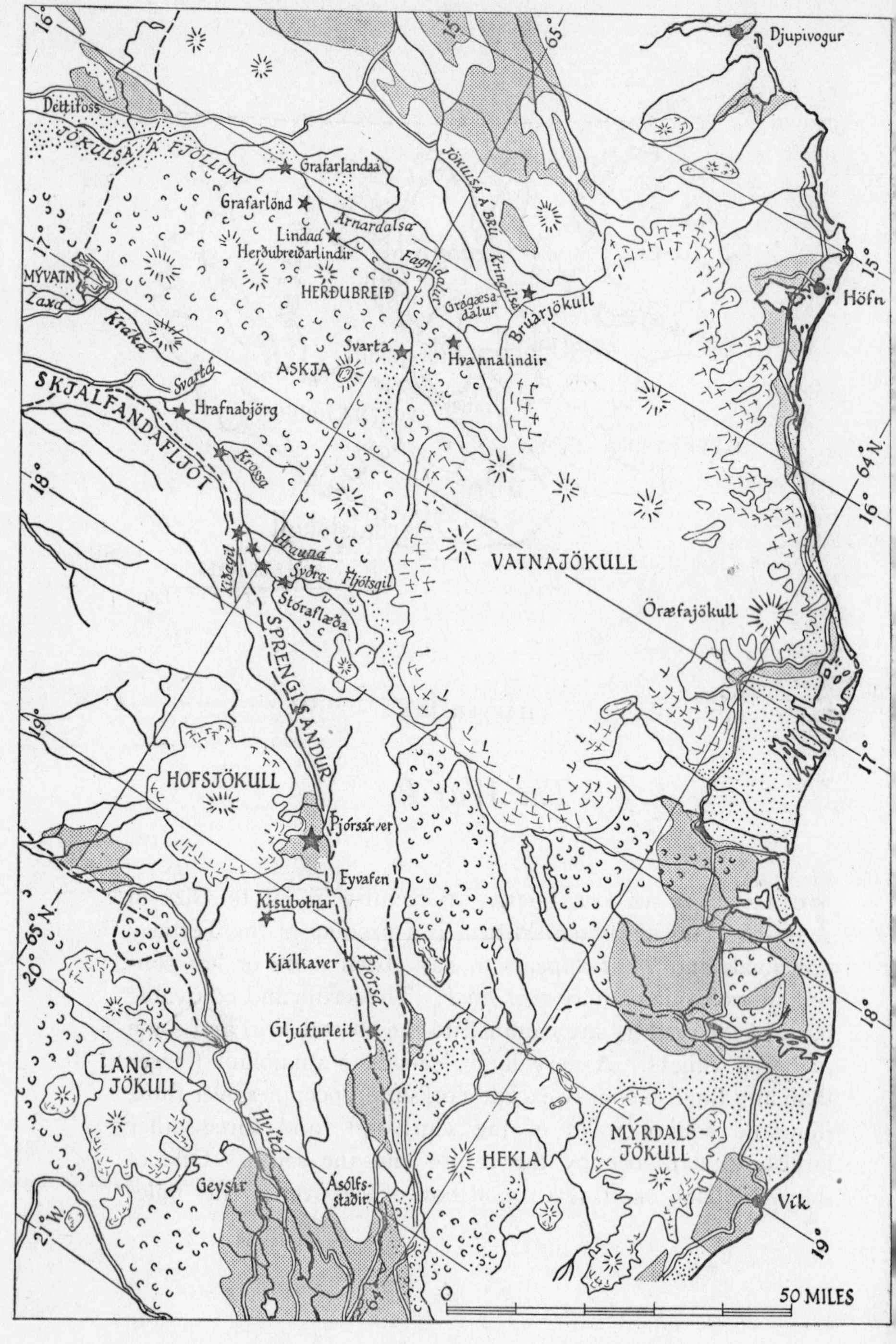

Djupivogur
Dettifoss
JÖKULSÁ Á FJÖLLUM
Grafarlandaá
Grafarlönd
Lindaá
Arnardalsá
Herðubreiðarlindir
HERÐUBREIÐ
JÖKULSÁ Á BRÚ
Kringilsá
Fagridalur
Grágæsa-dalur
Brúarjökull
Höfn
MÝVATN
Laxá
Kráká
Svartá
ASKJA
Hvannalindir
Svartá
SKJÁLFANDAFLJÓT
Hrafnabjörg
Krossá
Kiðagil
Hraunå
Syðra
Fljótsgil
Stóraflæða
SPRENGISANDUR
VATNAJÖKULL
Öræfajökull
HOFSJÖKULL
Þjórsárver
Eyvafen
Kisubotnar
Kjálkaver
Þjórsá
Gljúfurleit
LANG-JÖKULL
Hvítá
Geysir
Ásólfs-staðir
HEKLA
MÝRDALS-JÖKULL
Vík
0
50 MILES
16°
15°
65°
17°
18°
19°
20° 65° N.
21° W.
64° N.
64°

in diameter, which marks the very centre of Iceland. It crowns a central plateau at about two thousand feet above sea-level, to which the land gradually rises from north and south-west. Where it is not covered with snow, this plateau consists mainly of dark grey deserts of ash with occasional oases of arctic vegetation.

The summer melting of the Hofsjökull ice-cap feeds a big river, the Skjálfandafljót, which runs northward, and another river, the Þjórsá[1]—the biggest in Iceland—which flows approximately south-westwards to find the sea on the west side of Iceland's south coast, passing, as it reaches the fertile coastal region, through lands once owned by the heroes of the sagas—Gaukur Trandilsson, hero of the lost saga of Þjórsárdalur, whose great farm at Stöng was drowned in ash by the eruption of Hekla in 1104, and past Hlíðarendi, the home of Gunnar, the hero of the saga of Burnt Njal. This district between the Þjórsá and the southern ice-cap Eyjafjallajökull, one of the most beautiful and fertile in all Iceland, was covered with three inches of dark pumice in a couple of hours of the first morning of the latest eruption of Hekla, on 29 March 1947. But it was to the plateau in the centre of Iceland that our wild-goose chase led us.

The grey geese which breed in Iceland have been subject to frequent misidentification. Those nesting in the coastal farmlands and valleys have long been recognised as grey lags,

[1] Pronounced 'Thyorsow' to rhyme with your sow.

PINKFEET BREEDING COLONIES OF ICELAND

(*Map opposite*)

Symbol	Key	Symbol	Key
(shaded)	*Green Oasis*	(dotted)	*Sand and Rock*
(lava)	*Lava*	═══	*Road*
(ice)	*Ice*	- - - - -	*Track*
		★	*Pink-footed Goose Colony*

but only since 1929 has it been established that the geese of the interior—the *heiðagæs*—are pinkfeet. How these discoveries were made is described in detail in Chapter xvi, p. 179.

In 1950, when plans for the Severn Wildfowl Trust Expedition were being discussed with Dr. Finnur Guðmundsson, the eminent Icelandic ornithologist (in a Lapp hut in the mountains of Torne Lappmark, during a field excursion of the Tenth Ornithological Congress in Sweden), it was known that some two hundred pairs of pinkfeet bred in various colonies along the river gorges of the Skjálfandafljót and some of its tributaries. Guðmundsson had seen them nesting there. It was also known that pinkfeet had bred in the past and probably still bred in reduced numbers at some places along the courses of two rivers lying farther to the east—the Jökulsá á Fjöllum and the Jökulsá á Brú.

More important were farmers' reports of great concentrations of pinkfeet in late summer along the middle reaches of the southerly flowing Þjórsá, combined with evidence that the birds were breeding at the head waters of that river. Hatched and empty nests had been found on the terminal moraine [1] of the Hofsjökull where the glacial streams feed the Þjórsá through a complex of flat boggy meadows with unusually rich arctic vegetation. No real indication of the size and extent of the colony in this great oasis had been discovered. No ornithologist had ever visited it during the nesting season. Could this be the main breeding headquarters of the pinkfoot, since the known colonies in Greenland and Spitsbergen and beside the north-flowing rivers of Iceland quite evidently could not account for the total population of the species?

This was the exciting possibility which led us into the

[1] "Terminal Moraine": the rock-debris which falls on to the surface, or into the crevasses of a glacier, which is carried by the slowly flowing ice to the glacier's end, where it is deposited in a confused heap. When a glacier is "retreating", i.e. melting faster than it is formed (on an average), as are many of these in Iceland, their terminal moraines often occupy a wide belt.

Central Highlands of Iceland in the summer of 1951. Our plan was to explore this reported colony, to study and photograph the geese at their nests, and later to catch and mark as many as possible during their flightless period.

All birds go through at least one annual moult. Of most kinds, the big wing-feathers used for flight are shed and replaced by instalments, so that the bird is always able to get into the air and fly. But among the geese and ducks this is not so. All the flight-feathers are shed simultaneously, with the result that for an average of about three weeks in the year the adult birds are quite unable to fly. They can, however, run fast, swim and dive. The stage of flightless moult of the adults coincides exactly with the period when their own young are between one and five weeks hatched. For most of this period the young can run almost as fast as the flightless adults. Their leg muscles grow amazingly fast in their first few days out of the egg—much faster than their wings. Thus, on their breeding grounds, geese spend nearly a month in flightless family parties which often pool together and form great pedestrian flocks. It was among these flocks that we hoped to find some of the 634 geese we had ringed in Scotland, and to ring many new ones, both young and old.

For these purposes our equipment would have to contain nets and stakes, and, of course, rings. With a thousand rings we felt sure we should be able to deal with all the flightless geese we were likely to meet, and, privately, we decided that if we used less than a hundred of them the expedition would be a failure, but if we used two hundred it would be a success; to use five hundred would make it a complete and roaring success.

From the point of view of studying the nesting geese the problem of getting to our destination early enough in the season to be sure of finding them still incubating eggs was a difficult one. It was essential to arrive before the end of June, and only possible to travel by pony-train. Yet, in June, the snows would still be melting, and both snow-rivers and glacier-rivers full of water. Some of the oases on the way might still be snow-covered, and none might provide enough fresh growth to satisfy the horses. It would be necessary to camp for some weeks, and to carry a lot of equipment. It would also be expensive.

But in spite of these problems and difficulties, the Severn Wildfowl Trust Expedition finally set out from Reykjavík on 22 June 1951 in a large bus full of equipment. Also in the bus were the four of us:—Peter, the leader, Philippa (Talbot-Ponsonby as she then was), James, and Finnur, one of the best known, as we have said, and (he will not mind our saying so now) the largest ornithologists in Europe.

The bus brought us to the lower reaches of the Þjórsá and followed the road up the river's bank to the most northerly large farm, which is called Ásólfsstaðir. Here the farmer, Ásólfur, was expecting us and had prepared a good supper. Here the ponies were assembled (from this and neighbouring farms) which, on the morrow, were to take us and our equipment on the first stage of the eighty-mile journey up the river-bank to the oasis under the Hofsjökull, a journey which was expected to take four days.

For most of our bus ride it rained hard, but 23 June dawned with improved and improving weather. From Ásólfsstaðir we looked across at the great volcano of Hekla, which dominated the other side of the valley; its sides were still black with the three-year-old lava of the last great eruption, which had had no time to find any clothing of vegetation. In the still air a thin cloud of steam rose straight and high from a crater on the south-west side of the mountain, for it has remained mildly active ever since.

At half-past six on the morning of 29 March 1947, Oddur, the farmer at Heiði, about seventeen miles south-west of Hekla, went out of his house. He looked up at the mountain. It lay covered with snow to its peak; nothing unusual was to be seen. A northerly wind was blowing. He went to a haystack

1*a*. *Peter Scott at Ásólfsstaðir, the farm from which we started our journey into the interior.* (J.F.)

b. *Our guide Jóhann testing the crossing of the River Hnífá.* (J.F.)

2a. *Our pony-train crossing the desert.* (J.F.)
b. *Loading a pack-pony.* (P.T.-P.)

behind the farm and took a couple of minutes to cut hay for a cow. When he looked up again he saw that just on one side of the highest peak of Hekla there had appeared a yellowish-brown cloud, about five hundred feet high but growing rapidly. Ten minutes later there was an earthquake, and shortly afterwards the whole ridge of Hekla split, forming a fissure three and a half miles long, which immediately began to belch out lava along its entire length and to throw huge red-hot rocks high into the air. Very shortly the whole mountain was hidden in ash and dust. The eruption was at 6.40 a.m. At 7 a.m. the column of ash and steam rising from the volcano had reached ninety thousand feet, and it may have reached a hundred thousand feet a few minutes later. A little while afterwards the cloud settled down to a mere six miles in height! Sigurður Þórarinsson, the Reykjavík vulcanologist, who flew round the eruption at eleven that morning, found "voluminous cauliflower clouds, whose upper domes shone brilliantly in the sun while the lower regions appeared in a bluish-black colour. Glowing lava pieces were whirled high into the air, and lightning flashed through the ascending masses. Dark-greyish mud-streams wound their way down the slopes like gigantic worms, and these were followed by other broader streams, which crept steaming towards the plains below; these were the lava streams."

Those first hours of the great Hekla eruption of 1947 were of astonishing drama and beauty, and the people at Ásólfsstaðir, the farm from which our expedition was about to start, had a ringside seat. Fortunately, the wind was not blowing their way and they did not get the fall of ash that "drowned" a few farms in the south in those first few days. The rivers of lava flowed out of Hekla for a year and a month after the eruption.

CHAPTER IV

Journey up the Þjórsá

WE SPENT most of 23 June repacking our gear into three piles with the assistance—indeed, under the guidance—of our two farmer-guides, Jóhann Sigurðsson and Snjólfur Snjólfsson. One of the three piles would be loaded on to eleven ponies for the first trip in (making, with the riding animals, seventeen ponies in all); the second pile was to come in ten days or a fortnight later by a relief-train. The third pile consisted of a very large number of things which we were thankful to leave behind altogether. In the late afternoon the ponies set off, but without loads or riders, for people and gear were to go the first fifteen miles in two trailers, one towed by a jeep from the farm, the other by a tractor. It was about 5.30 in the evening before we finally said goodbye to the latest of a long line of Ásólfurs, and left Ásólfur's farm, Ásólfsstaðir, the jeep bulging with rucksacks and kitbags.

That first evening produced a mass of impressions. The whole scene was dominated by the great volcano to the east of us, and indeed it was with us for the whole of our trip, for from our final fixed camp, seventy miles farther on, we could still see it, with its cap of snow and its plume of steam. We quickly shook off the last real woods. (Woods are not perhaps quite so rare in Iceland as the books tell you, and round Ásólfsstaðir was a fairly dense piece of woodland with birches ten or twelve feet high, the home of redwings.) There was a level stretch of old lava desert flattened by wind erosion and crossed by hoofmarks and tyre-tracks. Our jeep had a puncture and, soon after, jeep and tractor, with their trailers, negotiated a little river, bumping over the big rounded stones on the bottom. On a meadow of grass by this river we came upon a bunch of sixteen pinkfeet feeding. The birds called with the familiar notes, but somehow strange in the new setting; they took wing, gained height, strung out and flew purposively up the valley of the river Þjórsá in the direction we were following. We wished them *au revoir*; and from that moment began to believe that the expedition *was* going to find what it was looking for. A black dog from the farm ran with us all the way to our camping-place, about fifteen miles, just for the fun of it. As we approached a fenced-off grazing place called Hólaskógur, three whooper swans rose from the edge of a stream, and nine pinkfeet from the grass above.

Camp was pitched in half an hour, which was not bad for our first tenting, with new and unfamiliar tents and in spite of a fresh breeze. Then we opened our first ration pack. We had brought with us British Army rations in compo-packs of ten man-days each. These were very convenient, as four of them made a neat pony-load of just the right weight. Only Peter thought the food disappointing at first, and that only for a few days. His previous expedition (to the Perry River in Arctic Canada) had been on American Army rations! But as time went on we all found the British compo most excellently balanced and satisfying, and even the guides, accustomed to Icelandic food, came to like it.

Next morning Finnur said: " I will now introduce you to your ponies." Phil, the best rider of the party, had a fine grey belonging to the wife of our guide Snjólfur. Peter had a small, quiet chestnut mare with a mop of grey mane cut in a fringe. James had a rather difficult black pony. Finnur, in view of his size, had about the largest horse in Iceland, a splendid piebald gelding but still only a pony. We reckoned ourselves

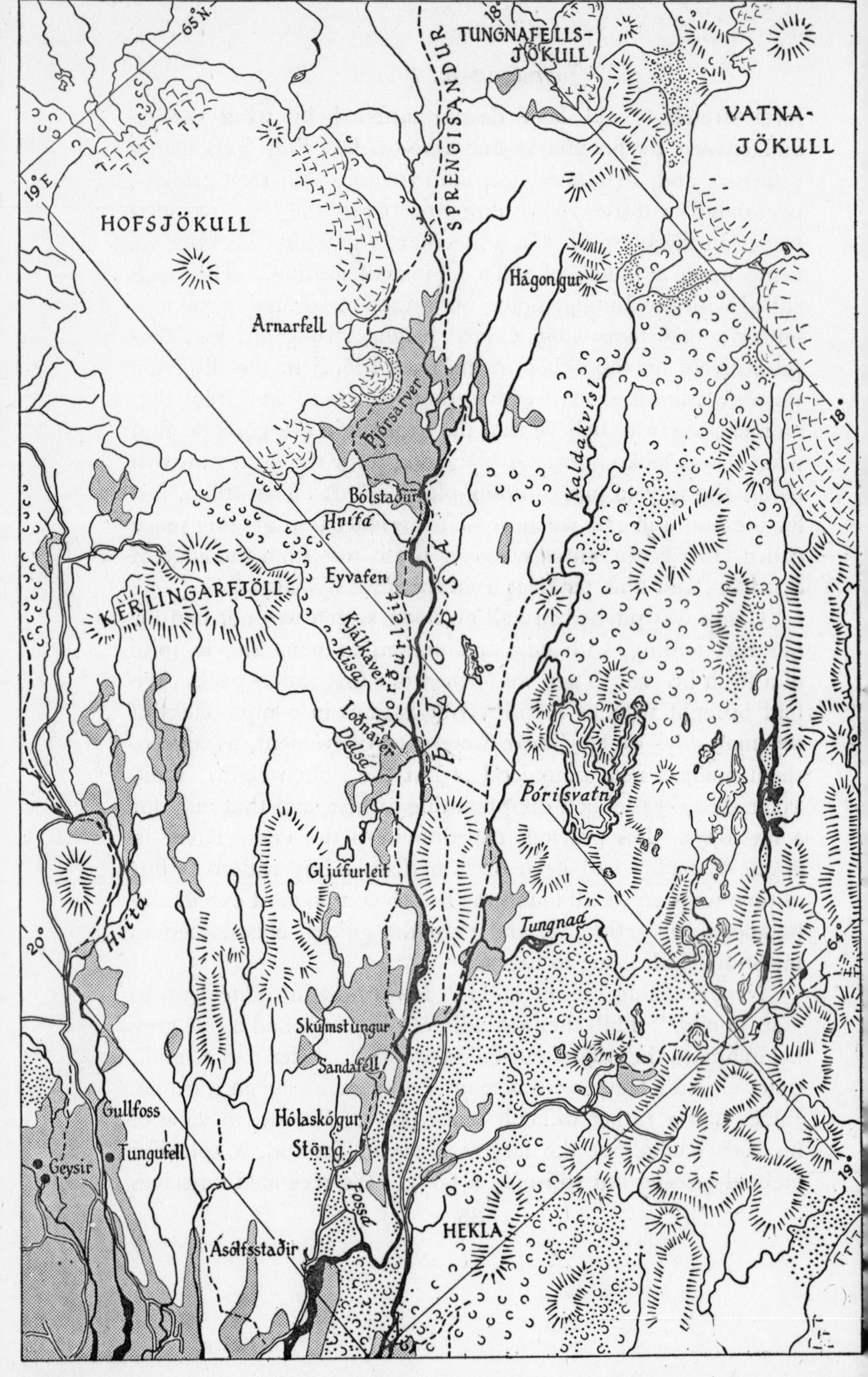

65° N.
18°
TUNGNAFELLS-
JÖKULL
VATNA-
JÖKULL
19° E
HOFSJÖKULL
SPRENGISANDUR
Hágongur
Arnarfell
Þjórsárver
Kaldakvísl
Bólstaður
Hnífá
Eyvafen
KERLINGARFJÖLL
Kjálkaver
Kisa
Þúfuverðurleit
ÞJÓRSÁ
Loðnaver
Dalsá
Þórisvatn
Gljúfurleit
Tungnaá
Hvítá
20°
Skúmstungur
Sandafell
Gullfoss
Hólaskógur
Stöng
Geysir
Tungufell
Fossá
HEKLA
Ásólfsstaðir
64°
19°
18°

lucky to be sorted out and packed in five hours, while a fresh wind blew across the desert before us, whipping up little sandstorms into angry browny-yellow pillars which rushed across the desert quite close to the camp, often forming a curtain between it and the Þjórsá valley beyond it and the snow-dappled slope of Hekla. We set off to a chorus of trilling whimbrel, plaintive golden plovers, purring dunlins, across a patchwork quilt of desert and the dwarf campion *Silene acaulis*. There were masses of *Dryas octopetala*, *Arabis* and thrift and a little single white bell-heather, *Cassiope hypnoides*.

We were moving into the interior a full month earlier than most normal travellers, in order to reach the geese at least before the majority of them should have hatched. This meant facing two difficulties, which are present in June but which disappear in late summer and autumn. The first of these was grazing for the ponies, the second, river-crossings. To carry food for horses on an Iceland journey means a great expense, because this food can only be carried on horses, which themselves require food. Thus, quite a small amount of horse-food may double the length of a cavalcade. The expedition had to rely on natural grazing, and only in a good season is this ready for horses in the interior plateau in June—and then only in scattered cases, special grazing places, the good ones always marked by a stone hut known as a *kofi*, in which the horses themselves can shelter and the men sleep on a stone ledge.

We camped by these *kofis*, on our way both in and out of the interior. As things turned out, the grazing was quite

---

ROUTE FROM ÁSÓLFSSTAÐIR TO HOFSJÖKULL
(*Map opposite*)

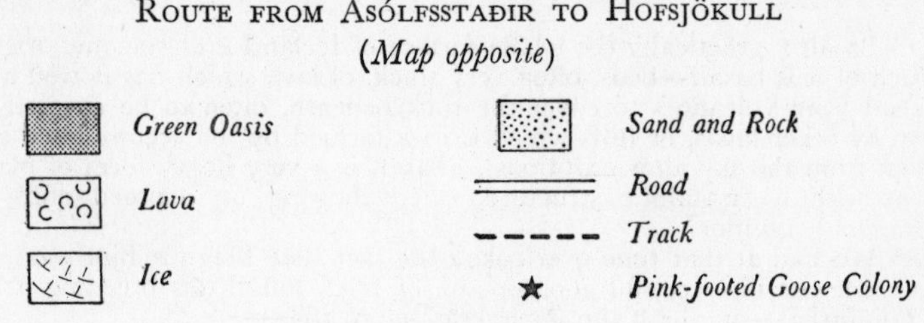

adequate, because it had been a rather forward spring, and while the horses sometimes got tired they could always find enough to eat.

The river difficulty concerned the lateral streams and rivers that flowed into the Þjórsá from the north-west, some of which were gathering water from large areas and many snow-fields. The snow-fields had been melting throughout a rather sunny June, and the guides foretold that some of these tributaries would be rather difficult to cross.

In the end, however, the only mishaps were ridiculous rather than serious. James, checking progress with a paper map, fluttered it between his horse's ears; the animal shied, depositing him on the ground, and galloped wildly about among the pack-train. James was unhurt. Peter, too, and his camera were undamaged when his horse stumbled and propelled both straight over its nose on to the sand. As time wore on the weather became more stable, until, during the last two days of the inward journey, there was no cloud in the sky, scarcely any wind and the temperature must have been well over 70° F. Not only the horses became distressed and hot.

We spent the night of 24 June on a rich meadow, eroded into gullies, on a steep hillside, Gljúfurleit, overlooking the Þjórsá, which here had a considerable fall and flowed through a gorge. At a corner in this gorge the fast river was swept to the left and had deeply eroded a series of precipices, pillars and pinnacles out of a bastion of black basalt.[1] Upon a buttress on this cliff over the river we found our first pinkfoot's nest—much lower down the valley than we had expected.[2]

[1] Basalt: practically the whole surface of Iceland is of volcanic origin. Much of it is basalt—beds, often very thick, of lava which has flowed and spread from volcanoes to cover the rock beneath, often to be covered in turn by other lavas, or tuff (which is rock formed by the accumulated ash fallen from the sky after eruptions). Basalt is a very heavy form of black lava, with a crystalline structure, often showing on exposed cliffs as hexagonal columns.

[2] We had at that time overlooked the fact that Magnús Björnsson, in his otherwise unsuccessful goose-season of 1931, found this breeding-place of Gljúfurleit—on about the same date, see p. 188.

Peter and Finnur saw it first, through powerful glasses, from a distance of nearly three-quarters of a mile across the valley; for a gander flying up the gorge went straight up to the nest, evidently to call the goose off to graze on a neighbouring hillside. For some time before they flew off, we watched both together at the nest: the goose sitting, the gander standing close by, its bright summer-pink legs hardly showing through a dense mass of *Sedum roseum* (rose-root, midsummer-men), the fleshy green and yellow plant that grows richly on many Iceland cliff-ledges.

After Gljúfurleit the way became desert in parts, often across stretches of sand and stone colonised only by little bosses of *Silene acaulis*, flowering most profusely on their south sides, the flowers very variable, some large, some small, some deep pink, some almost white. Occasionally we crossed real

carpets of the loveliest of all arctic-alpine flowers, the mountain avens, *Dryas octopetala*, with leaves of deepest green, and a yellow heart to a cream-white blossom that seemed to have its own source of motion on that windless day. We had struck the days of fullest flowering, and many beautiful alpines were in full bloom.

The main feature of this day was three whooper swans' nests; the great brown pile of moss of the first, with four orange-stained eggs, was incredibly obvious on the top of a little mound of lumpy tundra with two or three tiny pools round the nest. The second nest (at which the cob was not in evidence) was among a group of pools which had completely dried up; this, too, had four eggs. Peter stayed behind to photograph the third whooper's nest, at which the female crouched on the nest, trailing her head down the slope of the huge pile of moss, and even the male crouched down in a little hollow where he sat. After some serious trouble with the film magazines, three of which jammed, Peter advanced on the sitting pen and she crept off the nest at about sixty yards, and soon afterwards took wing, the cob with her. The nest was filmed (three eggs this time) and the footmarks in the red mud of the dried-up pools surrounding it. When Peter had finished the two swans flew past him and settled on a little tarn about seventy yards away. They flew from there again out of sight, but were back on the tarn by the time he got back to the horses and Phil.

The largest river crossing was the Dalsá, which unexpectedly was satisfactorily low and easy. There were pinkfeet in pairs flying or sitting thereabouts, but we had no time to hunt for their nests.

Peter, Phil and Finnur, after filming the last swan's nest, did not finally catch up with the pack-train till it had reached Kjálkaver at the confluence of the Kisa and Þjórsá, where we made our third camp. On the way they came upon a pair of harlequin ducks in quite a small clear stream. Peter tried to rig his camera to film them, but they flew just as he was ready; which was aggravating of them! The little ducks were very tame, though.

Kjálkaver, which means the meadow of the jawbone, was among a great sward of the glaucous willow and many birds. Grey lags flew over, and Peter called a pair of pinkfeet to alight within a hundred yards of the camp. James saw a pair of ptarmigan feeding along the river-bank after the sun had set, and found a dunlin's nest with four eggs. A long-tailed duck fished for water-animals in a shallow pond, which visibly contained caddis larvae, various daphnians and other small crustaceans, and the very primitive crustacean Apus (*Lepidurus*).

At sunset there were whimbrels trilling, and, to the north-west we saw the sharp peaks of the Kerlingarfjöll in silhouette. The Hofsjökull and the Vatnajökull looked incredibly beautiful, like great inverted saucers, with the light striking them differently, shimmering golden on the Vatnajökull and deep blue on the Hofsjökull's shaded side.

Two problems had now arisen in camp—the guides did not like the food, and the sleeping-bags were not warm enough. The two farmers enjoyed a supper of steak and kidney pudding, but did not care for the treacle pudding (although the Icelanders are supposed to be keen on fat and sweet things). Finnur was the chief sufferer in the sleeping-bag crisis, but we felt we should all be poorly placed if we met with really cold weather.

On the following day we started late in the afternoon, to avoid the heat of what was by then a Continental sun. Almost

Pair of Harlequin Ducks

at once we were in the Norðurleit, a real desert of sand and flattish plate-like slabs of stone which tinkled and clattered under the horses' hooves. The desert was black, grey and brown, mostly black, and it took over four hours to cross.

We stopped once to take photographs of the pack-train, or rather, the two trains tied head to tail—each bridle tied by a special knot to the flowing tail of the next ahead. Each string consisted of six horses, and the useless wild horse—one which refused to carry its pack—ran loose.

The ponies were noticeably more tired than they had been the day before. Once James's just sat down under him, and, later, Peter's little mare tripped and went down on her knees, and he, of course, went over her head. Although it was a stony part of the desert, neither of them hurt themselves.

We came to a tiny oasis beside a little stream. Finnur said: " Only the date palms are wanting." We expected to stop here for a meal before continuing, so we dismounted. There was a pinkfoot's nest with egg-shells in it; we thought it looked robbed but it might have been hatched. It was on a little lump of a mound, and the site was such as you might get at the outer edge of a salting on some British estuary—the vegetation battling with the sand.

For some reason Jóhann and Snjólfur decided the party could not wait here, and Finnur translated that we should all go on for a very short distance and then stop. Across more desert we came to another patch of vegetation along the banks of a larger river—the Hnífá (Pl. 1*b*, p. 32). The crossing of this was the most difficult yet, and the ponies were half-submerged, but they all came safely ashore. Here Jóhann decided to deviate from our plans, and led off to follow along the Þjórsá instead of cutting across towards the Hofsjökull. This was disappointing, but he was concerned with pony-feed and his judgment had to be accepted.

As we came up the edge of a stony patch, we found a small pool at the foot of a snowdrift. Here were five broods of baby geese with their parents—3, 2, 2, 6, 3. They ran uphill across the snow and on over the crest. On a headland by the edge of the river we saw a gander walking almost towards us. Presently he flew as if wounded, fluttering along the top of the water of the river. At first we thought he was moulting, but it was a definite case of injury-feigning, and a few minutes later we saw his mate leading two young ones away from the nest. She had left three more in the nest, not yet strong enough to follow her, and this in itself illustrated the danger of disturbing newly-hatched goslings. The female defended the young most bravely, and Peter photographed her with wings spread and feathers ruffled at a range of about five yards. Then we caught the two goslings and returned them to the nest, where we photographed them (Pl. 5*b*, p. 64) and moved on as quickly as possible. At many points along the river we saw broods of geese.

The first sight which brought home to us, more than anything else, that here might be a special concentration of wild geese, was a slightly sinister one. On a sandbank in the Þjórsá stood half a dozen great black-backed gulls. A pair of arctic skuas moaned about the moor. The guides found a dead arctic fox. These were the parasites upon the goose population, the snappers-up of neglected eggs or unconsidered

Pinkfoot Goslings

goslings. And as we came round a bend in the river-bank, a huge brown bird flapped across the water and alighted, yellow-legged, alert and cruel-looking, on the opposite bank—a young sea-eagle, not yet in white tail.

We came at last to a *kofi*, a small turf-roofed hut, standing opposite a shallow stretch of mildly broken water in the river. This was the lowest ford of the Þjórsá. Here we hastily unloaded the ponies at the edge of a marsh full of ridges and pools, in which quantities of pinkfeet were nesting. We had no idea how long we should be staying there—but we expected it would only be a matter of hours; so we made the mistake of camping without due selection of site. We decided to pitch only the main tent; we planned that we would all sleep in it, and that Finnur, James and Peter would keep two-hour watches on the ponies, in order that the guides could get some sleep. A watch was very necessary for at any time there was a risk that, hobbled though they were, the ponies would suddenly take it into their heads to set off for Ásólfsstaðir, and the fact that their forelegs were tied together made, as we were soon to discover, distressingly little difference.

Before we went to bed we explored the marsh a little. We found a number of hatched nests, one of them only six feet from the main tent, and three pinkfeet still sitting. All their eggs were chipping. Finnur, on his way down to look at the river level with Jóhann, found four more nests with eggs.

Jóhann explained that the river Blautakvísl was uncrossable here at its junction with the Þjórsá owing to the unusual flow caused by the four days of hot sun, which had melted the glacier.

On 27 June, after the first night at the edge of the tundra meadows of the Hofsjökull, we realised that we were camping amongst one of the denser concentrations of breeding pinkfeet in the oasis, and that the oasis must in truth contain the missing breeding population we were looking for.

CHAPTER V

The Great Oasis

THE GREAT OASIS we had reached occupied a complex of boggy ground with very lush vegetation considering that it lay about two thousand feet above sea-level. The Danish geodetic survey, in the days when the King of Denmark was also the King of Iceland, had made from ground and air a pretty adequate map of Central Iceland, and from this and from our notes and sketch-maps we calculated that the true oasis was as much as forty-four square miles of vegetation surrounded by a vast desert of basalt and lava-sand and the permanent ice of the great Hofsjökull. The oasis itself was separated into different meadows by branches of the various glacier-streams which flowed from the ice-cap into the Þjórsá. These streams were known as *kvíslar*, and the biggest of them—big enough to hinder communications quite seriously—were the Blautakvísl and the Miklakvísl. These various meadows or *vers* all had names. The night's camp was in Tjarnarver, the meadow of the tarns. Beyond the Blautakvísl was Oddkelsver, the meadow of the farmer Oddkel—some ancient visitor. Beyond the Miklakvísl were Illaver (the meadow of bad going—very boggy), Múlaver, the meadow of the hillocks (the terminal moraine of the Hofsjökull glacier), and Arnarfellsver, the meadow of the eagle's mountain. Collectively these meadows may reasonably be called Þjórsárver við Hofsjökul (the Þjórsá's meadows at the temple glacier).[1]

The boggy tundra that occupies most of the flat plateau of the *vers* is a true tundra with underground ice in some places. Its dominant vegetation on the drier ridges is the glaucous willow or sallow, which creeps, dense, up to six inches from the ground, and makes long, woody, underground roots; and in the bog-hollows cotton-grass and sedges.

Everywhere are reminders of the action of frost and snow that operate on the face of this queer land for eight months out of the twelve. Frost and weather have made polygons everywhere—stone-polygons, mud-polygons, and the bogs themselves are polygons. The mud floors of many of the dried-out tarns are marked with footprints—made by the feet of whooper-swans, geese, goslings, dunlins and in some places of man (our own).

Here and there is evidence of the protective action of snow against frost, for on some steep banks of hollows that have held deep winter drifts the display of flowers is specially rich and varied—great swards of dandelions, buttercups, rose-root (at its best just at this time), the daisy *Erigeron uniflorum*, many heads of the white alpine chickweed, purple cranesbill (sometimes very dense and pretty), pink-white cuckoo-flower, yellow *Potentilla*.

On the stony hills and more rocky, barren places—also on sandy places—are tufts and small blankets and pincushions of *Silene acaulis*, the ever-present little pink campion, and the white bladder campion, *Silene maritima*, flopping on the desert in lazy abandon. Sorrel; the sorrel-like *Oxyria*; many white heads of *Arabis petraea*, a common rock-plant here; and a whole

[1] Used thus the word Hofsjökul is in the dative and therefore only has one l.

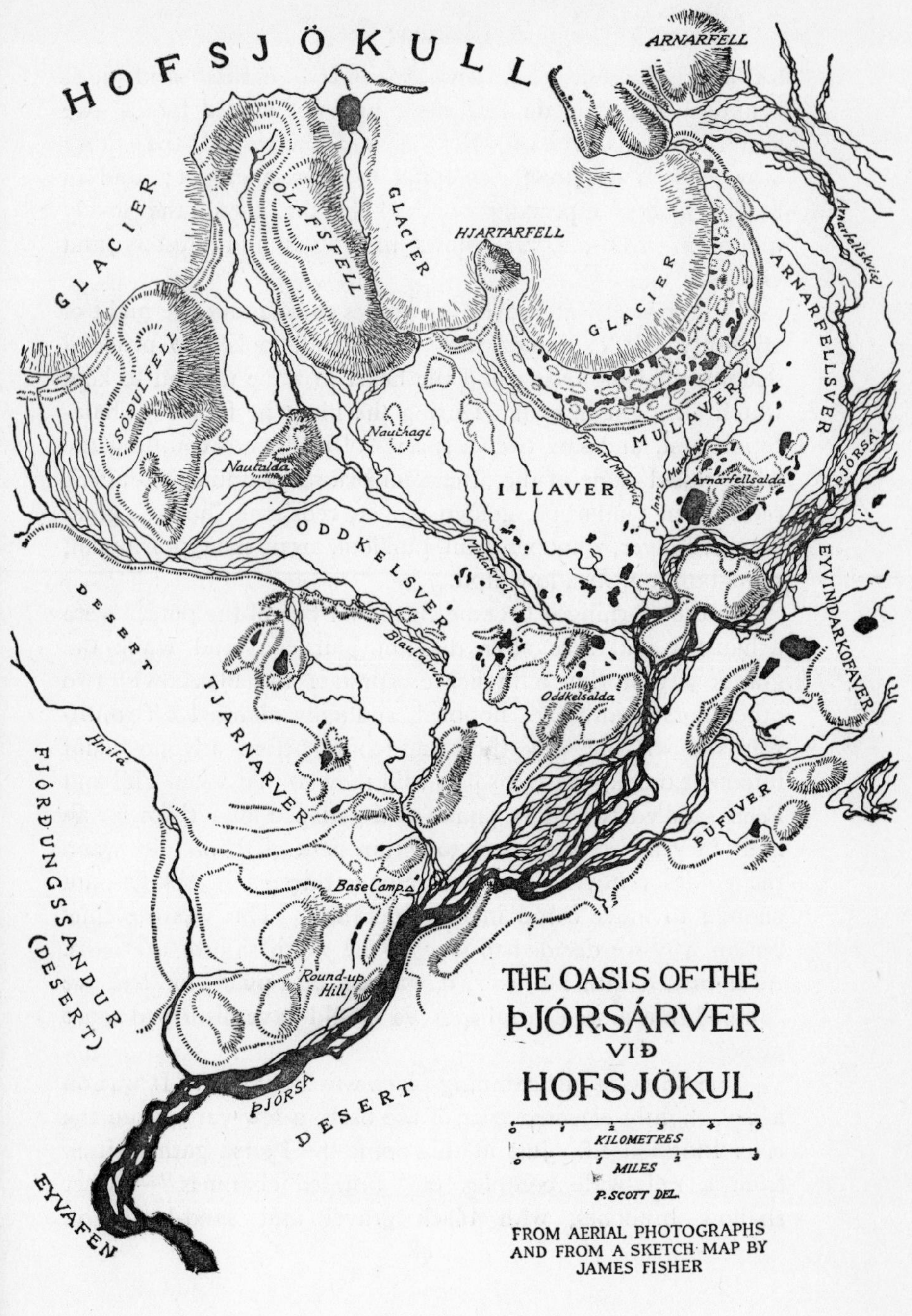
HOFSJÖKULL
ARNARFELL
GLACIER
ÓLAFSFELL
GLACIER
HJARTARFELL
GLACIER
Arnarfellskvísl
ARNARFELLSVER
SÖÐULFELL
Nautalda
Nauthagi
MULAVER
Fremri Múlakvísl
Innri Múlakvísl
Arnarfellsalda
ÞJÓRSÁ
ILLAVER
ODDKELSVER
Miklakvísl
EYVINDARKOFAVER
DESERT
Blautakvísl
TJARNARVER
Oddkelsalda
Hnífá
FJÓRÐUNGSSANDUR (DESERT)
ÞÚFUVER
Base Camp
Round-up Hill
ÞJÓRSÁ
DESERT
EYVAFEN
THE OASIS OF THE
ÞJÓRSÁRVER
VIÐ
HOFSJÖKUL
0 1 2 3 4 5
KILOMETRES
0 1 2 3
MILES
P. SCOTT DEL.
FROM AERIAL PHOTOGRAPHS
AND FROM A SKETCH MAP BY
JAMES FISHER

lot of saxifrages. (*Saxifraga oppositifolia*, earliest and most beautiful of the arctic saxifrages, had not waited for us—we found only its fruits.) In the meadow round the camp crowberry is dominant, creeping to form a carpet; and in banky places, especially overlooking the river, the lovely mountain avens, *Dryas*, blows in singles and clusters and groups.

Finnur kept watch over the ponies throughout the night of 26 June. He explained that we had all looked so peaceful sleeping that he hadn't had the heart to wake us, and so kept watch all night himself. During the night he found a phalarope's nest, and saw twelve species of birds, not counting the white-tailed eagle of the afternoon before: dunlin, whimbrel, red-necked phalarope, golden plover, redshank (heard), great northern diver, whooper swan, pinkfoot, arctic skua, ptarmigan, snow-bunting, meadow-pipit.

In the morning it became clear that two of the ponies were exhausted and sore after the hot journey; and while the guides were trying a higher crossing of the Blautakvísl two other horses, although hobbled, suddenly charged off southwards down the way they had come before anyone could intercept them. Indeed so fast did they go that when Phil and Peter saddled two more ponies and galloped after them for an hour they never even came to within sight of them. So, when the guides returned, there were only thirteen horses fit—not enough to move camp in one operation. This was the chief reason why we decided to stay at the south side of the oasis. As it turned out, however, it was the best place, for had we camped in a more central spot we should have disturbed more geese.

The name of our camping place was Bólstaður. It was on a dry, slightly elevated part of the oasis, a few yards from the river Þjórsá itself. Just at this point the Þjórsá gathers itself from a mile-wide complex of "braided channels"—rather shallow branches, with black gravel and sand-banks in

Peter Scott (leader). (P.T.-P.)

James Fisher. (P.T.-P.)

Philippa Talbot-Ponsonby (and Whooper cygnet). (J.F.)

Finnur Guðmundsson. (J.F.)

3. THE MEMBERS OF THE EXPEDITION

4*a*. *The Base Camp in the oasis with the Icelandic and Union flags, and the Icecap beyond.* (P.T.-P.)

b. *Nest of Pinkfoot, 26 June 1951.* (P.T.-P.)

between—to a quarter-mile wide stretch of gentle rapids flowing between steep banks. The bank opposite the camp was a green hog's back known as Sóleyjarhöfði or Buttercup Headland. Between Bólstaður and the Buttercup Headland there is a well-known crossing-place of the Þjórsá which the autumn shepherds ford on their horses. The ford is marked by a *kofi*. There was a pair of snow-buntings nesting in a crevice in its wall and a pinkfoot's nest on its turf-covered roof.

On 28 June Peter and James dashed off articles for *The Times* and the *Manchester Guardian*, and letters home. The guides were hanging about, rather anxiously, drinking coffee, waiting to return. At last they were able to get away. Peter filmed the cavalcade of ponies as it disappeared over the little hill. Their return, with the second instalment of our gear, was promised on or before 10 July. Peter and Finnur set to filming a nearby pinkfoot from a hide. The four of us had the centre of Iceland to ourselves for nearly a fortnight. Without horses it was not going to be possible to explore every part of the Þjórsárver.

The first days were spent in exploring the home meadow, Tjarnarver. All over it pinkfoot goslings, newly hatched, and dry, were running with their parents. Such goslings as were caught were, of course, far too small for leg-rings which would have slipped off their little feet at once. These were tagged with the new Swedish-type wing-clips, which are fairly easy to handle—a bent stainless steel pin with an aluminium label, folded at the edges to make an attachment like the clasp of a safety-pin. The pin is threaded through the skin of the gosling's forewing, behind the web tendon and in front of the bones at the elbow-joint. This was quite harmless, and apparently quite painless, for this particular part of the gosling's anatomy appears to be devoid of blood-vessels or nerves (see Pl. 5*a*, p. 64).

These were busy days, finding and counting nests, measuring eggs, tagging goslings. There were enormous individual differences in behaviour between the geese. Some females went straight back to their eggs the moment the humans were out of sight; others took hours to return. One female was away from her newly-hatched and hatching offspring for so long that a foster-goose had to be found to take the deserted brood, and she ended up with no less than eleven goslings, which she looked after very well.

In a few days the main tent had been shifted to a new and more satisfactory position. We ran up an aluminium mast for the wireless receiver-transmitter, with which we made intermittent contact with Reykjavík, two hundred miles away. On the wireless mast we ran up the Iceland and Union flags, and their agreeable and familiar colours played and waved against the white of the ice of the Hofsjökull. Later we were to see our flags (and Peter to film them) against yellow sunsets and orange sunrises, against the red-brown and white of the Kerlingarfjöll (the old women's mountains) in the west and the black-and-white of the Tungnafell, the Hágongur and Vatnajökull to the north-east, and Hekla to the south; against dark rain clouds and white cumulus. But in the early days of the camp the weather was hot and anticyclonic, the sky cloudless. The sounds round camp were always of birds, and either of wind or of insects. There were many flies, including the black fly *Simulium*, an American species which gets no farther into Europe than Iceland. There was a bumble-bee, and four kinds of moths. We had brought effective insect-repellents, so we were not much troubled by the biting elements of the insect population. The area of this camp belonged to a meadow-pipit which sang its display-song continually; and we were visited by the cock snow-bunting from the *kofi* three hundred yards away. Sometimes he sang in

flight, sometimes from a bank—a cheerful little song somewhere between that of a corn-bunting and a hedge-sparrow. We put up a hide at the *kofi* later and filmed the male and female snow-buntings as they fed the young.

The pinkfeet usually kept quiet at this time, unless they were disturbed, when we would hear their double honk—*ang ang*. The whooper-swans, when they were disturbed, uttered curious sad trumpetings that could be heard at a great distance. But saddest of all the sounds were those of the arctic skuas, which cried like lost children, and the continual lost cries of the golden plovers.

Peter's diary for the afternoon of 28 June reads:

" As we followed the Blautakvísl upstream we found that it divided to form a large island, but the stream on our side of the island was unmapped. We looked out across this island from a low hill, but our view was restricted by a heat haze. The Catalina flying-boat from Seyðisfjorður to Reykjavík passed over the marsh very high, but a great many geese got up. One flock of twenty-four flew round, and evidently some of the breeding geese were disturbed because, in the far distance, we watched a great blackback robbing a nest. He took the eggs up to a height of about fifty feet and dropped them. On one occasion he was attacked by an arctic skua (most of them are the dark form). When this happened, instead of taking the egg to the river gravel, he tried to break it by dropping it in the marsh. Evidently this did not work, as he took the same egg up three times. At the third time he did not feed on it, but instead went back for another. Perhaps it sank deep into the marsh and he could not get at it, or perhaps he was not hungry enough. He was driven away from the nest by the persistent attacks of the skua.

" We lunched at the top of the next hill, overlooking a

new valley and marsh leading south from the Blautakvísl into Tjarnarver. A brood of well-grown (seven-day) goslings ran up the far bank, and away over the hill. There were six of them as they ran out of the stream at the bottom. Below on the marsh was a swan's nest, with the pen slinking away to a tarn beyond. There was what looked like an arctic tern sitting on a little point in one of the many pools. Finnur thought it unlikely, but we waited until after lunch to go down into the marsh and find out. During lunch we saw a very distant sea-eagle flying over the tongue of the Hofsjökull with a large pale bird mobbing it—probably a blackback or perhaps a light form arctic skua—it was too heat-hazy to be certain. We ate corned beef and biscuits and cheese and jam, and then went down to the stream and drank at a wonderful spring of dark, cool water up-welling in the mud of a tiny pool surrounded by *Carex* and moss, the up-welling making a queer round patch in which the grains of sandy mud trembled and shuffled and shivered. Yellow *Saxifraga hirculus* abundant here.

" The marsh below us was rich in birds although the pink-feet had not got a strong colony in it. The swan's nest had five eggs. There were lots of dunlins, but we couldn't find a nest. There were red-necked phalaropes on the pools and arctic skuas hawking about, and we flushed two pintails from fresh eggs.

" The white speck we had seen *was* an arctic tern—we found her nest. Sitting beside this tern was a dunlin. It sat there, within six inches of the tern, whenever she was on the nest. I filmed her there, and then we went over the hill in order to try to let the swan back on to her nest."

On 29 June the weather was still fair but the prospect was less promising—at least, from the point of view of comfort. From the point of view of communications, a cold spell was desirable; for the hot weather of the previous week had melted the glacier so rapidly that the *kvíslar* were unexpectedly full and deep. This meant that the crossing of the Blautakvísl, which the ponies had failed to find, was going to be quite a problem on foot. Finnur contrived a level mark by the bank which told us when it began to drop. Peter thought of trying to cross at the place where it entered the Þjórsá itself. Here it spread out into a wide delta and it looked possible to cross from sandbank to sandbank, in places more shallow than higher up. After two hours of pottering, Peter found it was quite possible to cross in thigh-boots, and the rest of the expedition followed him; those of us who did not have thigh-boots wore waterproof trousers tied round ordinary Wellingtons. Phil got a trickle of water in one boot, but the others got over dry, and for the first time we stood in Oddkelsver, after

many knights' moves from sandbank to sandbank to find the shallowest elements of the much-split river.

At once we were among a near-colony of goose-nests, and began quickly to find and note them. It started to rain (the first rain of the expedition) and we had a wet lunch in mackintoshes by the empty bed of a spring torrent where Peter swore he saw a purple sandpiper and James said it was probably a dunlin. After lunch we worked over to the west side of the hill Oddkelsalda and at once Peter recognised the note of a barnacle-goose. We saw it flying off low with a pinkfoot. They appeared to have been flushed from a nest, which was afterwards found; it had eggs—three heavily set, one rotten. It appeared to be a male barnacle mated with a female pinkfoot; it was marked down for photography. Many dunlins and goldies were to be seen, and in one place we saw a dunlin pursued by three arctic skuas at once—it got away.

On the way back Phil and James got their boots full crossing the Blautakvísl; they were careless because of their first safe crossing.

Peter's diary for 30 June reads:

" It rained fairly extensively during the night, but the day dawned fine, with the cloud clearing and intermittent sunshine about noon. Finnur planned to stay in camp, blow eggs, etc. James planned to tidy up the camp—dig a gash-pit, make various receptacles, and hoist a Union flag on the radio mast. Phil and I planned to ford the river again and set up hides beside the near pinkfoot's nest and also by the barnacle's nest. We set off so heavily laden that I decided not to take rain-clothing. As we reached the edge of the Oddkelsver marsh there was a pair of golden plovers against the background of the Hofsjökull and with them some dunlins. I filmed all these and also a dark phase arctic skua. We took the hide to the pinkfoot's nest and the bird was very docile. At about twenty yards she stayed on the nest while we rigged up the hide and left it without disturbing her. As we walked up the sands (so as not to disturb the nesting birds on top of the marsh—and the relation of marsh to sandflats here is very like that of salting to estuary in Scotland) a pair of great northern divers flew up the Þjórsá very high and calling wildly as they went.

" There is a river—almost like a creek—which winds into the marsh to within a few hundred yards of where the barnacle was nesting. We followed this river in order to reduce disturbance to its minimum. At the mouth of this creek was a male long-tailed duck, which flew down past us against the strengthening south wind. Farther up the creek we came upon two small drab waders with dark marks just in front of the eyes. I felt sure they were purple sandpipers, and this was confirmed when a dunlin came and sat down beside them and gave them scale.

" As we approached the barnacle's nest the heavy grey

clouds which had been gathering behind us began to deposit their rain, gradually, steadily, and utterly drenchingly.

" When we spied the barnacle's nest the female pinkfoot was sitting and the barnacle's white face appeared above the *Salix glauca* as he kept guard. On the pool just short of the nest, where yesterday three whoopers had settled, there were three broods of goslings. One party of three disappeared at the back. The other two families merged—six goslings—and walked round the mud at the left of the pond. We held back in order to give them time to filter away, but two crouched. Almost at once a great blackback appeared and took one of the goslings, although it was only a few feet from the pinkfoot gander. This was only about seventy yards from us. The great blackback carried the gosling a few hundred yards away and ate it —being dived on the while by an arctic skua. Having eaten it he returned to the pond.

" The second gosling was out in the middle of the pond in very shallow water. The gull stood near it. The blackback was first a friend in the eyes of the gosling, who ran towards it, then became doubtful, then ran away behind a tiny island. The gull was not hungry; he washed his bill and drank, pranced up to the gosling once or twice, but left it. The gosling made its way across the pond to our side. Meanwhile, a pair of pinkfeet had returned and an odd gander. The three were standing on the far side of the pool about seventy yards away. I think that when the two broods merged one pair took away four of the six young, and left the other pair dispossessed. Anyway, this pair stood on the far mud while I walked over, caught the crouching gosling, tagged it and released it towards the pond again. At first it would not go, but crouched, and I had to shoo it into the water. Then it set off across the fifty yards of water, the pair calling all the while. They waited for it and led it away gently while we held back to give them time.

" I did not want to wait too long, for the barnacle's female had already left the nest, and in the rain the eggs would cool quickly, also they had got to get used to the hide, which might take an hour or so. We put the hide up and withdrew at once. By this time the rain was heavy and continuous. We stopped when we got down into the creek again to eat some chocolate and a sodden biscuit, and then threaded our way down the creek and back along the Þjórsá sand. We met the long-tailed drake again, and later a diver settled in front of us in a shallow lead. It seemed too small for a great northern, and I thought it might be a redthroat, but there was too much rain to use glasses.

" Phil walked suddenly into a nasty quicksand, and I walked into another later. They are so extremely local that they could be very dangerous, I think. The Blautakvísl had risen three or four inches, but we got across without trouble, and returned to a tidy welcoming camp—I soaked to the skin, but not so Phil, who had sensibly taken rain-clothes.

" James cooked an excellent supper of fish pie. At 11 p.m. we switched on the radio again. That morning Finnur had fiddled with the set (as I had done extensively the day before), and had found some spare fuses. We changed the fuses, although there seemed to be nothing wrong with the ones we took out. Later James had fiddled with the tuning and had at last produced a reading on the aerial output dial—thus we were in much higher hopes of success. So when, by 11.10, we had heard nothing, we were very disappointed. Having called us last night, we thought, maybe they would wait for two nights on the every-other system. Finnur said he thought we should listen a little longer, so I passed the phones over to him, and at about 11.20 he heard Gufunes calling us. Finnur and James wound the generator handle in turn like demons, and eventually we established pretty shaky contact. Later he became easier to hear, and so apparently did we, in spite of the bad atmospheric conditions. We asked the time (when he had failed to get a longer message) and were given it at 23.36. Then he asked us to pass the main message again and at the third or fourth attempt he got it. It was to tell the British Minister that they were in radio contact with us. With a plan to talk to each other again to-morrow night at 23.00, we signed off. It was a really great triumph, coming as it did on top of so many disappointments, and we went to bed feeling on top of the world, in spite of the tearing rain-squalls."

Rodent-run by Dunlin

CHAPTER VI

The Ice-Cap

THERE FOLLOWED SEVERAL days of bad weather, and for a good deal of the time the expedition was confined to camp, except for short dashes to inspect nests already found and to tag a few whooper cygnets. On 3 July, when out for a short walk, Peter watched a dunlin doing a " rodent-run " injury-feigning performance, accompanied by a squealing quite unlike the normal dunlin voice. But 4 July was very fine, and we decided to walk to the ice-cap at Múlaver, near Arnarfell. James's diary for the long day runs:

" We walked twenty-six kilometres in about fifteen hours, starting from camp at about 11.30 and returning at about 02.30 on 5 July, just as the sun was rising. It was wonderful; for most of the time the weather was sun and cumulus, with little wind. The reflected light and heat from the Hofsjökull appears on still days to create a patch of blue over it even when the rest of the surrounding part of the world is clouded.

At times we could talk gently to each other at a hundred yards, and the absence of wind and rain made the cold night enjoyable, even though it froze.

" The Blautakvísl crossing went like clockwork, and we went through S.E. Oddkelsver to clear off the pinkfoot hide and tag any goslings available (one only). On our way we found early on, in a pool, a red-necked phalarope in winter plumage together with a very dark female in summer plumage, and these we photographed almost *ad nauseam.* We left the hide in a creek, and took the slanting crossing of Oddkelsalda, which led us past our lunch-place in the wet of 29 June. Here we confirmed that Peter was indeed then right about the

Red-necked Phalaropes seen together on 4 July

purple sandpiper; for we were quickly in the territory of one, which came tamely flying towards us in a business-like way, with a rather sharp " whick whick whick," and a trilling purr that was almost a rattle. This was the first we encountered holding a territory, though later we were to find them on the borders of Tjarnarver and Hnífárver. The habitat of this species up here is *off* the tundra-bog and *on* the more barren, alpine, dry, well-drained hillsides, where there is a respectable amount of vegetation, especially provided by sheltered banks and gullies, and where there is gravel, stone or broken rock. Very similar to the raised beaches and foothills of Spitsbergen where they are so common. We pushed on, up a gully which made a natural road, over the water parting and down to the

Miklakvísl overlooking now the eastern corner of Oddkelsver, from a trough passage through which one could ride a horse unseen by the tundra-geese on Oddkelsver. This may be very useful for future netting. We showed ourselves, perhaps a little too early. There were plenty of geese, some with broods. They moved off west, while we plunged down to the crossing.

" This was prospected, in the usual style, by Pioneer Peter in his boots, gum, thigh—trying the delta approach so as to take the stream in instalments. We worked far out in the delta so as to be practically in the Þjórsá. Peter carried Phil over the worst bit(Pl. 6*a*, p. 65), and my trousers stood up to several above-knee passages. Finnur's didn't, and he went wet-foot for most of the rest of the day, uncomplainingly. We staggered ashore (the crossing took half an hour) at a mossy corner of Illaver and had a good lunch by a tarn of clear water. Before us stretched a great flat bog in which we could see geese and swans, leading apparently straight up to the semicircular moraine, though we knew there was another river, the Fremri Múlakvísl, in between.

" On Illaver we saw our first flightless geese, nine of a party of twelve on a longish tarn-lake which we reached soon after the crossing. Peter walked up one side of the lake and the rest of us up the other, but eight of the nine broke off the water, ran over the bank, and away into the meadow very fast, before we could get near them. The other remained on the lake, and swam about with its head and neck stretched on the water.

" A pair of swans basely deserted two cygnets of about a day's hatching when we were over 200 yards away, and left them swimming in the middle of another largish tarn. As we got on, the footing got iller and iller. Illaver is a very sticky bog, and it was necessary to zigzag across it on the harder ridges between the patches of bog. But occasionally the supply of ridges gave out and we had to plunge our way across *Carex* and *Sphagnum* growing in mud that sucked and spluttered and sank and shook under us. But we won through (even heavy-weight Finnur did not get stuck), and met a pair of dark arctic skuas with a single egg on the way, and arrived at the banks of the Fremri Múlakvísl amid a chorus of purring dunlins, moaning skuas, plaintive goldies, bubbling whimbrels and twittering phalaropes. We photographed a flock of seventeen of these just before the crossing.

"This was again bravely prospected by Pioneer Peter, and he carried Phil across safely. Finnur had no trouble, apparently; but I got properly wet through being careless and overconfident. However, the sun was shining abundantly, and at 19.25 we crossed a corner of Múlaver, which is narrow at this part (and very fertile and full of good grazing) and sat in glorious shelter, illuminated by the slanting evening sun, at the farthest point reached in the past by the glacier (a full kilometre from where it now ends), a terminal moraine clothed with earth and vegetation. The willows grew some three feet high, and there was promise of lushness in the new growths of *Archangelica*, and one bank, against which we hurled a full broadside of camera, supported a rich thick jungle of *Sedum roseum*, some yellow, some red at the heart, and all of a curious fat green of leaf, and all set about with buttercups and *Potentilla*. Finnur found a new plant, *Arabis alpina*.

"The moraine behind this terminal tangled bank is disappointing. 'Like the moon,' said Peter. Hardly a plant; giant's gravel of grey stones, for miles laterally and nearly a mile transversely. Every now and then a piece of red rhyolite shattered and scattered into a score of fragments by frost. Very hilly and daly, and in the middle exactly, between the glacier edge and the *ver*, a chain of long lakes with shallow crossings between them, fed by melt-water streams from the glacier which cut down through the gravel hills of the moraine. Finnur tells us that most of the retreat of the glacier has been in the last thirty years—a whole kilometre from the tangled bank to where it now is. The whole "moon-area" of gravel and gravelly hills is a desert, probably because the plants have not had *time* to colonise it. Must make some botanical notes on our next visit.

(Later our guide, Valli, remembered his first visit to the glacier twenty-six years ago, when the ice-front was only about thirty metres from the overgrown front of the moraine. No wonder few plants have been able to colonise the moon-like territory! What a chance for a botanist interested in ecological succession.)

" Finnur and I went right up to the ice-cap and walked on to it where a tongue came down between two morainic banks, about 100 metres on to a convex slope where the strain had forced the ice into blue and blue-black corrugations and crevasses of smallish size and depth, but of incredible complexity. It would have been difficult to get through them. Finnur and I photographed each other on the ice, like railway passengers at the top of Snowdon, Finnur assuming an air of humorous intrepidity. There were very blue tarns just where the ice-cap ended, into which it was melting, very blue indeed, and from them the streams cut down through the moraine; on our way back we followed one down and it cut through a less dead part, being colonised by *Silene* and *Salix herbacea* and (at the stream) *Sphagnum*, and here we were visited by a purple sandpiper that owned a territory, in the usual way of such birds.

" We all gathered together again and sat on the evening sunny bank and had another meal and made happy jokes, and then started homewards at 19.25, this time taking a more easterly course so as to have more of Múlaver, and better footing across Illaver. We soon ran across four goslings which we marked and a goose's nest (empty and hatched) on Múlaver which had been built in the cup of a last year's whooper nest. Some of the ordinary goose nests in Múlaver were on traditional sites; i.e. obviously of several years' standing, on banks guanoed by the geese, and green as a result. Our crossing of the Fremri Múlakvísl was lower down this time, and cleaner, and we found ourselves on the dry side of Illaver, near hills much larger and longer than the little white lozenge on the map. Here came a moment of importance. We were working south to the Miklakvísl, along a moss-polygon flat (with ten- to twenty-foot polygons between which some depressions were six feet deep), and working west of the hill we shall call Illaversalda, when we saw some geese and broods crossing a stream-mouth between us and the hill, where the stream entered the Þjórsá, and making up the hill. As they crossed the stream one adult had no white on its tail; it looked queer, and then in a streak of evening light as it turned up the bank it looked red. Distance about 300 metres, with glasses, good light behind. Phil also looking, told Peter to look too, cried out "red"; but Peter, who only saw the bird on the skyline for a fleeting moment before it reached dead ground, thought it looked red but could not be quite sure. Phil was quite sure; so was I but didn't say so until I'd heard her say so, which was craven but circumspect. Red tails mean Dumfriesshire, March 1951, dyed by Peter, Hugh Boyd, Geoffrey Percy, John Yealland and Phil after a catch with rocket nets.

"We passed a lovely knoll with a natural moat on its south side and a flat platform with a tangled bank of *Sedum* and other plants above it—a wonderful natural camping-place though possibly a little wet, with good water. All part of the west end of Illaversalda. On our way from here to the Miklakvísl crossing we picked up and tagged two goslings that we had seen on a tarn (and thus been unable to catch) on the way out.

"The crossing was interesting; I went on ahead, knight's moving from sandbank to sandbank on the delta until almost in the Þjórsá. I stumbled once in a soft patch, but the anorak kept most of the wet out though I plunged my sleeves in up to the shoulder to steady myself. Eventually I got over-booted and soaked. The river had risen a little; but I had changed my socks and was waiting on the opposite bank by the time the others got across, Peter dry in his thigh-boots with Phil carried; Finnur wet with no dry things to change into, but quite imperturbable. Back over Oddkelsver, up the Oddkelsalda corridor, turning back to see (midnight) the after sunset behind the ice-cap, and a pair of whoopers rise, whoop and circle before it like a painting by Peter, which only goes to show that his paintings are true! Entirely still—the voices of the others at the crossing reached me 300 metres away. Began to be cold but not at all unpleasant. We passed the purple sandpiper again and paused for a drink in his territory; slanted down into S.E. Oddkelsver, kept under cover, picked the hide up from a creek we had left it in (J. F. feeling strong) and marched along the sands to the Blautakvísl. As we shook the water off our boots on the gentle slope from the river to the camp it was 02.30 on 5 July, and there was hoar frost in a clear sky, and the audible quiet of windless frost. The dominant sallows had turned from green to almost white, changing the landscape entirely to a sort of Christmas colour, for in the frost their leaf-groups had closed to show their lighter undersides, and upon them was white hoary dew. A tiny tinkle of ice in the water-bucket. Hot drinks and a quick hot meal, I forget of what (? bangers, we were not very hungry). We were enormously happy and satisfied with our quite long walk, and soon went to bed and slept for ten hours.

"*5 July*. In camp. A bath by a tarn and washed some clothes. Phil kindly washed some of mine, too. Writing, reading, eating, wasting time talking, others smoking. Got radio both ways in the evening. Prepared a list of the birds of the Þjórsárver við Hofsjökul, to be added to as we go on. (See Appendix C, p. 206.)

6 July. Bad weather; stayed in camp in morning gridding maps and making calculations about the area. Peter called us out of the tent to watch an arctic fox on Sóleyjarhöfði opposite.

5a. Fixing Swedish-type wing clip to patagium of newly-hatched Pinkfoot gosling. (P.T.-P.)

Brood of five newly-tched Pinkfeet, 26 June 1951. (P.T.-P.)

6*a*. *Crossing a glacier river—the Miklakvísl—Finnur with Peter who is carrying Phil.* (J.F.)

b. *The Kerlingarfjöll in the evening.* (P.T.-P.)

It trotted slowly along the bank, and came to a goose's nest that we had previously observed to be occupied (sitting 3 July). Perhaps the nest had not hatched; perhaps the young were away leaving a rotten egg behind—whatever the case, the fox played with, and eventually ate, an egg in the most leisurely fashion, and afterwards curled up on the downy nest and went to sleep for twenty minutes! Finally it trotted off over the hill, in no kind of hurry."

We worked away in camp at journals, nest records, tagging data and the results of our transects (counts of nests observed in chosen strips of oasis). We realised we might not be able to rely on these transects very much, but we felt we should use every available method of arriving at the numbers of geese breeding there. If we could get some idea from the visible broods and cross-check with the empty nest estimates, we might finish up fairly near the truth. James was very keen on this work and spent the day with his slide-rule on the problem. Finnur went off to have a bath in one of the pools in the marsh, and returned, more or less rain-soaked, to announce that he had undergone a rebirth. Peter shaved, a little reluctantly, as, although this was not his first shave, his beard promised each time to be better than either James's [1] or Finnur's—though they hadn't shaved at all.

The day was spent very agreeably in the big tent, which was a light and cheerful place. We played five in a row noughts and crosses, and James played Patience with two packs, and Finnur and Phil read Whodunits. About eight-thirty in the evening it stopped raining, and Phil, James and Peter went for a walk to get an appetite for supper, while Finnur dug in various parts of the marsh to find the frost level, which in some places he found to be at forty centimetres. By August it would be farther down, if there at all, so that we were in doubt whether to call the marshes tundra or not.

[1] Nonsense (J. F.).

James christened them Gooseworthy Tundra-Bog, in assessing the area to be counted in the estimates of nest numbers.

Peter's diary for the next days:

" *Sat. 7 July.* A grey day with occasional drizzle but no serious rain. When Phil went down to the Þjórsá to wash there were eight non-breeding geese sitting in the river-bay near camp and two broods of young feeding near the mouth of the iron-coloured stream that flows into it.

" We spent the day exploring to the south-west of our camp, that is to say, back down the Þjórsá and up the Hnífá (the Knife River). We divided into two parties in the hope of one driving flightless or young geese to the other. James and Finnur went down the Þjórsá bank, while Phil and I stalked over into the head of a marsh, the marsh where we had had such difficulty trying to catch the pony—the marsh which meets the Þjórsá near the first pinkfoot's nest we found with small young.

" Up at the head of the marsh we could see broods of geese in three places—three broods over on the far hill, three broods down in a hollow between, and two broods among some lumpy ground below us. We decided to stalk up to the two broods among the lumpy ground, and went, first, round the wrong side of a lump, having to retrace our steps. We were getting fairly close to these two broods when a pair of whoopers began to make loud alarm-notes. They had one cygnet with them. This set the geese moving, and we were still 300 yards away. There was not a hope of coming up with them, so we turned aside and caught the cygnet. The pen was not at all brave and left her white downy baby when we were still 150 yards away. This cygnet was the first I had seen close to. A baby whooper is an extraordinarily attractive creature —the palest of pale greys—almost white, with a peaky bill mostly grey but with a patch of flesh colour near the base. Surprisingly, the legs are quite bright, orange-pink. We tagged it. Phil went to the nest, which was quite close, and found two eggs, still unchipped and therefore evidently rotten, in it.

" A few hundred yards farther down the valley were two small tarns, and on one of these a pair of red-throated divers had two young. I saw the young ones with one parent from afar in the glasses—indeed, before we tagged the cygnet. But as we came down to the pool the two adult divers were alone. On the near side of the pool was a light phase arctic skua, which was evidently concerned at our presence, although it did not go through the flopping antics of the pair in Illaver. It kept settling in front of us and in one place it appeared actively to be tending some egg or young bird underneath it, although when we went to the spot there was nothing. I could not decide whether this had constituted deceptive behaviour or not.

" At the edge of the pool was a hook-shaped peninsula and on the inside of this—in the harbour, as it were—the red-throated diver had its nest. The two tiny black young ones tumbled into the water and one immediately dived. The other swam out—bill held at about thirty degrees to the horizontal—but made no attempt to go after the parents, which were about fifty yards away across the pool. We could see the marvellous patterning of black and white lines up the back of the neck; and in the glasses the extraordinary upturned bill, tilted up and held at this strange upward angle, came once more as a surprise—a sort of caricature of my memory of the bird. One of the parents continually uttered a croaking bark. This was the larger of the two and from other indications appeared to be the male. For instance, the smaller one was moving in a much more agitated way. Presently they both took off and flew low over us, looking exquisitely graceful. The female made a perfect landing on the next pool below, and in a few minutes was up again, settling beside the young, one of which immediately dived as if afraid of its mother. Farther down the marsh was another lake, with some tundra mounds, on which we found an empty pinkfoot nest. We flushed a dunlin, but could find no nest or young. It is very strange that we have only found one dunlin's nest with eggs since we arrived here (from horseback in our home marsh), because undoubtedly the dunlin is one of the three commonest birds of the area. Pinkfoot and golden plover are the others. The dunlins are very often in close association with goldies, and this relationship would be worth studying. 'Plover's page'; in Icelandic *lóuprœll*, plover's slave (thrall). They are appropriate names. There must be some fairly highly specialised behaviour mechanism working here. My guess is that it is in the dunlin's behaviour pattern rather than in the plover's. Whether the fact that both have black bellies in summer plumage is significant I don't know. We have had several examples of dunlins fraternising with other species—purple sandpipers, for example. And there was the dunlin which enjoyed the close company of the incubating arctic tern in Pintail Marsh. This curious phenomenon should be worked out.

"There were a few phalaropes in this part of the marsh and three female long-tailed ducks on the large pool. We met James and Finnur near the bank of the Þjórsá and set out along the sand to head off a pair of whoopers with two cygnets which were making an overland passage across a shoulder of hill. As we came up the river-bank a pair of swans (one of which had been asleep) rose from the bare willow scrub. This was not the pair with the cygnets, but we came upon the second pair a couple of hundred yards beyond. They were in a hollow, and took off almost as soon as they saw us. After they had gone the two cygnets came towards us, but at about ten yards they decided, on breasting a ridge, that we looked dangerous and began to make off.

"We caught, photographed and tagged them; and then it began to rain. I had not brought my movie camera and was bitterly reproaching myself, for even in the bad light two broods of swans, the divers and the light phase skua were sad things to have missed.

" Having put on our waterproof capes we started up the slope of a hill—a bare stony hill—and suddenly over the top we saw two broods of geese quite close. We gave chase, shedding gas-capes and rucksacks as we ran. As we came over the ridge we saw two broods making off—one went to the right with five young, and one to the left with seven rather larger young. The pace was hot. The goslings, especially the larger ones, ran about as fast as we could. The female of the right-hand family stayed running in front of her brood with out-stretched wings until I was about twenty yards from her. We caught four of these, and the one we missed was the first to crouch and must have been somewhere behind us. This aspect of brood catching is important. One must get all of one brood, or at least one pair of adults must fly off broodless. They will then return and collect the goslings. If, however, they go away with even one young one they will cut their losses, because they go on leading the one young one away and never go back for the rest. This, at any rate, is how we think it works. In this case we were certain that the right-hand parents had flown off without young. Meanwhile, James had caught one of the seven-brood, and Finnur and Phil and I had caught another after a wild serpentine chase over the rocks in which the gosling showed incredible stamina. The first and last were the larger birds thought to belong to the brood of seven. They must have been at least two weeks old.

" When released the six went off in a tight little bunch and without panic. On the stony ridge beyond I could see a single gander standing, almost waiting for them.

" We retired round the hill and came over a different way, to a sheltered lunch place under a bank, where there was a shallow pool of pretty nasty water. These picnics have been very pleasant. We take with us a can of corned beef, a can of margarine and a can of cheese, some crisp bread and biscuits, and sometimes some cake. We finish up with chocolate and sweets, a cigarette, a short rest and on we go again.

"Below us was the valley of the Hnífá, with the gentle green slopes of Hnífárver topped on each side by the grey stony hills—*alda* is the Icelandic name and it means a wave; the grey stony waves.

"As we came down to the river which runs over rapids in a rocky bed, we saw a bunch of about ten geese. They evidently could not see us well, for they were unusually tame, standing and looking at us for several minutes. We were still 500 yards away. When eventually they flew, three were left. These tried to fly and it seems that they only now realised that they were flightless. They hastily swam across the river. Even then their behaviour was curious. The first to land scuttled up the bank and set off at a round pace over the *Salix* flats beyond. The other two dallied on the bank, then walked quite slowly up among the broken edges of the low cliff. Finally they started off quite slowly across the *Salix*. We were sitting down watching, so that I am sure nothing occurred to scare them more, but suddenly the two seemed to generate an urgency. They walked faster and faster until both were scuttling away as fast as the first.

"We followed the left bank of the river—the east side. I was telling an interminable story about the war which was totally inappropriate to this beautiful place. Presently we caught a glimpse of a dark-coloured duck flying up the river. Round the next corner was a picturesque waterfall, and sitting below it was the duck, a female harlequin. She was sitting at first on a rock, but as we approached by way of a low headland with a hatched and empty pinkfoot's nest on it, she jumped into a foaming pool. She sat there for a bit and then, about forty yards away from us, she started up the waterfall. It was amazing to watch. True, she flew up the main fall itself—a height of three or four feet, but she landed in the very swiftest water at the lip of the fall. There was a further ten yards of rapids which almost amounted to fall before the smooth water above. She set out to make a diagonal passage across this, actually diving across some of the spouting jets of water. It was quite unbelievable, and when, towards the end, she got bored with it and flew twenty yards up to the calmer water, we just stood there amazed. When she settled she swam to the edge and disappeared round the corner. Then she peeped back, just to see if we were following, it seemed; although, actually, she cared little for our presence. She was very tame. James stalked up with his camera, but she flushed from under the bank and he only got her flying low across the river.

" For the next mile up the river we found pinkfoot nests on almost every suitable site. A headland protruding into the river was favoured, and if it had some eminence that was an added advantage. Most of the nests were hatched, with empty shells and membranes among the nest down. Some had been robbed, with broken shells, broken from the outside, and in quite a different way from a hatched shell. Many nests had both types of shells—often one destroyed egg-shell only. This single egg predation which we have found very commonly here, most probably indicates an addled egg which was eaten by the predator after the rest had hatched.

" We found ten empty nests, but none with eggs. At one place we set off to pursue two flightless adults who were running, together with two unmoulted adults with a brood. We could not catch up with them at all, and soon lost them among some rocks. They may have crouched, but it is doubtful. We must wait till the horses arrive before we can hope to catch up with these moulting birds. After this pursuit James found that he had worn some blisters, and so he and Phil headed for home, while Finnur and I walked on for a while to make a slightly longer circuit.

" We found an island in the Hnífá which had two this year's pinkfoot nests, but it had evidently at one time been a much stronger colony as there were at least seven old nest sites.

" At one place on the river a golden plover did the best injury-feigning I have seen from this species here-up (as Finnur would say). The bird sat normally in front of us, then the tail was depressed, slightly at first and then sharply down to the ground. Then the wings began to droop, one more than the other. Then she flitted across the river, both legs dangling; and once on the other side, she ran through the scrub in a very plausible rodent run. The male joined her and also performed a rodent run. Then the female came back and repeated the performance exactly.

" The Hnífá ran through a narrow pass with a steep gravel slope on our side. Here there was a pile of ptarmigan feathers. In the soft black sand around it there were two sets of prints. There were deep slits at the tips of the three toes. Finnur put his hand down and it barely covered the great footprint. The white-tailed eagle had recently fed here. Parts of the entrails of the ptarmigan were still quite fresh.

" On a marsh below was a pair of dark-phase arctic skuas. From the hill side we watched the female go back on to her nest. It was too far off our course to be worth visiting. From here we turned back and walked across desert hills, past occasional tarns and vegetation. At one pond we came upon the tracks of James and Phil returning. I noticed that they divided and appeared to be running, and I wondered what they had found here an hour or so before. Perhaps a brood of geese, for there were tracks and droppings of adults and goslings. At one point we saw where the geese had brooded their young, presumably overnight. The little droppings of the goslings were clustered round the droppings of the female. There were two such places, perhaps two broods or perhaps the female had moved for some reason during the night. I noticed an interesting thing about the droppings of the female. It is, of course, well known that birds leaving a nest during incubation make exceptionally large droppings. We have found that these are seldom more than thirty yards from the nest in the case of pinkfeet; so that if you find these greatly enlarged pear-shaped droppings you may know that there is a nest close by. This has been one of our methods of finding hatched nests. (Another has been the patch of short broken droppings left by the gander as he stood guard.) But the female with these goslings (which were eight days old, as we shall see) was still making the pear-shaped droppings. It seems, therefore, that the enlargement of the cloaca, caused by egg-laying, persists at any rate for eight days after hatching, but it may be that the enlarged droppings are only made at night, when the bird might not wish to excrete frequently because of disturbance to the young she is brooding.

" The whole question of nest sanitation in geese is of great interest. It appears to be subject to very wide individual variation here, because it is recorded that the nests of barnacle-geese are always surrounded with excreta.

" Some Ross's nests on the Perry River were more or less constructed of droppings in a sloping heap. Here some nests have had droppings close round them, but the majority have been quite clean, although often with a great mass of the gander's droppings within a few feet. Many nests on traditional sites have richer vegetation round them, but I have noticed at least two nests with this rich vegetation—mostly grass—round them and yet with no droppings. This suggests that they have been used by a different bird from the one which originally manured the surroundings.

" Finnur and I returned home in great spirits, Finnur telling me of the summer he spent in an eider colony on an island on the north coast, of the spectacular way in which the eiders first went on to the top of the island from the shores, at high tide one evening, how they only stayed running about on top for a few minutes (this he acted by running about and stopping as we walked). From this he went on to tell me of eider colonies in general. He told me that the largest had been a mainland colony of 10,000 pairs, but the farm had changed hands and it was not now nearly so strong. There were several of 5,000 pairs, but the numbers varied from year to year. He told me of the efforts made by the farmers to retain their eiders—how one had written a paper in 1870 about care and treatment of an eider colony: Eyjolfur Guðmundsson. Music was used, musical instruments which sang in the wind; coloured ribbons on strings, and so on. All these were supposed, and still are by many farmers, to attract the eiders. Perhaps they do. An eider's down is taken twice, once just before the eggs hatch, when the lining of the nest is taken, and then later after the young have gone. Each nest is worth twenty kr.—about 8s.—so that a colony of 5,000 pairs is worth £2,000 annually. Some farmers have a way with eiders, others not. They always go dressed the same, follow the same route through the colony, and so on. The down is now sent to a central cleaning place and fetches 1,000 kr. per kilo.

" Finnur described in detail just how tame the eiders were; how his tent was pitched before laying time, and how several selected sites under the guy-ropes of the tent. He made this study in 1940, and he told me he had not yet published the results. I suggested he might do so as one of the proposed new series of *Scientific Publications of the Severn Wildfowl Trust* which James and I have been discussing recently. He said it was a good idea but that he had a much more important paper on the ducks of Mývatn which he must do first, and that he would let us do it. This would be a most wonderful addition to the series we are planning. Discussing it brought us all the way back to camp.

" Here James and Phil explained the mystery of their running footprints round the tarn. It seems that they had surprised a brood of geese and had only managed to find one gosling, although they had seen three. The parents had flown off and apparently flew round solicitously. The gosling they caught, which would otherwise have brought the total to fifty tagged, turned out to be a recap—No. 521 marked as a day-old on

Oddkelsver on 29 June (one of a brood of five tagged in the rain). James and Phil agreed that the gosling was unexpectedly small considering it was known to be eight days old. By this standard the six we caught earlier in the day must have been at least fourteen days old or more.

"After supper we got Gufunes Radio to admit that they heard us, but they stopped trying in a very short time."

CHAPTER VII

Peter's Diary: The Guides Return

" *Sun. 8 July.* A lovely hot morning. We all sunbathed outside our mess tent. For the first time the flies have begun to be really troublesome. It's not that they bite—much. An occasional one does; but the main trouble is getting them in one's eyes, mouth, hair and ears. They are a bore, but still only a minor bore. There are a good many species—all small dark Diptera. Some are quite black, others the same as the ones at Mývatn, with grey bands on their legs, *Simulium vittatum.* There are also blowflies of a different kind from the English ones, and dung-flies which look just the same as their English relatives. There are beetles with a green thorax and brown wing-cases, and other round beetles which are small and black. One species of moth—possibly a *Plusia*—is fairly common, and there are at least two other Noctuids and more than one species of Geometer.

" After an idle morning, lying in the sun and writing up notes (how difficult[1] this is with so congenial a party, with so much pleasant talk and constructive discussion), and an early

[1] We counted ourselves lucky to have kept up to date with our diaries and notes during this trip. In most scientific field expeditions note-book time exceeds actual field-time—and if the time spent writing up data and conclusions for publication, on return home, be also included, the field-naturalist almost invariably finds that for every hour of observation he has mortgaged ten hours with pen, brush or slide-rule.

(for us) lunch, Phil and I set off to photograph the baby red-throated divers. We got held up on the way photographing flowers. When we reached the Diver Lake only one young bird and one parent were to be seen on the water. I think the adult was the female. As I was filming her from the bank at fifty yards' range I heard a strange harsh squeaking coming from the far side. When I went round I found at once the

Whooper Cygnet
(*Cedric, who shall be nameless*)

other baby diver. It was sitting on the shore about ten yards away from the nest. It raised its bill as if to beg for food when I approached. I filmed it and then went on to film the adult with the other baby in full sunlight at about forty yards. This should be quite good. Phil photographed the baby on the shore, and then I caught it and we tagged it, filmed it in the hand to show the way the legs come out of the very hind end of the body, so it seems. The down was very dark blue-grey, bill, legs and eyes black.

"We moved away up the hill beyond the lake so as to let the diver back to its second baby as soon as possible. We saw it climbing ashore when we were three or four hundred yards away.

"As we came into sight of the upper pools of Chipping Swanmarsh (the swan's nest had contained chipping eggs on the day we had first visited it) we saw a pair of swans with one cygnet. This was quite evidently 543 (Cedric, who shall be nameless). They made off down the marsh. At one point they had to run the gauntlet of an angry arctic tern through whose nest territory they were evidently passing. The tern dived on them time and again, and at every dive the adult swans ducked. It was an astonishing performance, and quite evidently the swans didn't like it at all. When they finally got through they started overland, trailing little Cedric, to the next set of ponds in Chipping Swanmarsh.

"We went over the ridge and surprised a pair of pinkfeet. They flew round and round and evidently had a brood or perhaps a nest. Their behaviour indicated that they had been disturbed before and we did not go hunting for their goslings because we thought it quite likely that they were the recaps of the evening before.

"The alarm notes of this pair of geese must have been heard by the swans of nest T [9] because, when we topped the ridge, both birds were far out in the marsh. I filmed them as they flew up the valley. We went to the nest, and found that the three eggs were not covered, which was rather remarkable since the bird had left the nest on a pinkfoot's alarm-note. We wondered whether perhaps some swans at least do not cover their eggs, or whether her departure had been more hurried than we supposed. While photographing the nest the pen came back looking magnificent against the brilliant light shining down over the Kerlingarfjöll, and reflected from the pools in the marsh. She settled about 100 yards away and whooped in melancholy fashion every ten seconds until we had disappeared back over the ridge.

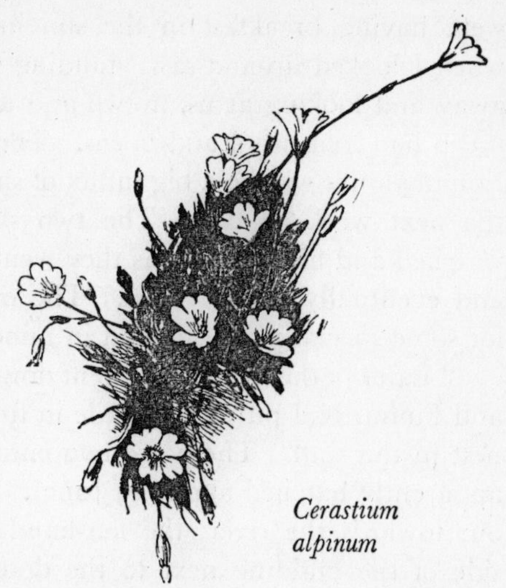

Cerastium alpinum

"For some time there had been heavy rainstorms hanging about; indeed there was so little wind that hanging about is just what they did. One such had been hanging over Nauthagi (a place in Upper Illaver) and Upper Oddkelsver for an hour or more. Now it extended, more than moved, towards us. There was a brilliant rainbow, for the sun continued to shine in under the raincloud. It did not rain for long, because suddenly the cloud above had spent itself and dissolved and vanished over us. Once more the sky was blue overhead and the flowers glistened, and it was warm again. We came slowly home to camp, taking pictures of *Silene maritima*, *Cerastium alpinum* and *Dryas*.

"In the evening we made some kind of contact with Gufunes Radio. 'You are very weak,' he kept saying. 'Will you give me a long tuning-call.' And so James and Finnur took it in turn to wind the handle very fast—a most exhausting affair for them. At length he signed off: 'Understand you have no message for us. We have no message for you, will call again at 23.00 to-morrow night.'

"We still have not passed the position of our camp, which we are anxious to do.

"*Mon. 9 July.* Just such another day as yesterday. We

were having breakfast in the sun just outside the mess-tent when I looked up and saw, standing not more than 100 yards away and looking at us, a ewe and a well-grown lamb. The sheep had long wool and horns. These were the first of what Finnur thinks will be a big influx of sheep into this area during the next week or two. The two sheep trotted on and we watched and filmed them as they went down to the Blautakvísl and eventually swam across. The ewe was evidently bound for some special place she had in mind.

" Later in the morning I went down to the *kofi*, where James and Finnur had put up the hide in front of the snow-buntings' nest in the wall. There are two entrances to the nest (which apparently hatched about 29 June). The right-hand one goes out towards the river, the left-hand one on the downstream side of the building next to the door of the *kofi* itself. This *kofi* is a house made of stones, with a timber roof covered with earth. There is quite a rich flora growing on walls and roof. The *kofi* has a door but no windows. It consists of a single chamber, with a raised shelf across the dark end on which, presumably, the shepherds sleep. The shelf is occupied by saddles and other equipment for the horses at present, and a shelf along the back which is a kind of manger has Finnur's specimens on it.

" I put some saddles in the hide to sit on and installed myself for three hours, during which it became so hot at one period that I had to take my jersey and shirt off, and so cold a little later that I was quite perished.

" The snow-buntings came and went. I filmed them and made notes. The most interesting points were that the female always entered by the right-hand entrance and left by the left-hand one, whereas the male only used the left-hand one for coming and going. The female came more often than the male. Sometimes she brooded the young. The excretions of the young were brought out and not eaten, so far as could be ascertained. Most of the food brought was black and

7a. *Spying from Oddkelsalda with the braided channels of the Miklakvísl, Upper Illaver and the Hofsjökull in the background.* (P.T.-P.)

b. *Site of ancient goose-fold on hillock, Illaversalda, with the River Þjórsá in the background.* (J.F.)

8. *Ancient goose-fold on Nautalda.* (J.F.)

probably entirely insect food, but the female brought one feed which was entirely green. (Later we found that this was insect food too—sawfly caterpillars which both male and female snow-buntings found quickly on the glaucous willows.)

"At twelve minutes past three, when I had been almost three and a half hours in the hide, James came down to see how it was going. The female snow-bunting had been sitting for twenty minutes. She flushed off, and we moved the hide in closer before returning to camp for a belated lunch.

"Now I am sitting in the tent and am alternately too hot and too cold. This morning's showers have persisted, and it is raining now, with a cold draught coming in at the door. Not many minutes ago it was almost too hot to stay in the tent. There was a pattering on the tent roof then, but it was from inside instead of out. Several hundred assorted flies have come into the tent and they show a marked positive phototropism, that is to say they follow the sun round, crowding into that corner of the tent roof nearest to the sun.

"But when it starts to rain their pattering ceases, and now the loud rattle of the rain drums on the tent roof. James has just returned drenched from his measurement of the home goose-nesting area. Finnur is in the hide watching the snow-bunting, and I am up to date with this journal for the first time for DAYS. Hurrah!

"We are expecting the ponies with the second lot of our food to-morrow—10 July. That is the day they promised not to be later than. Of our twelve Army food-packs we have eaten seven. These seven boxes represent 70 rations, and we have eaten them at the rate of six people for the first three days (18 rations) and four people for thirteen days (52 rations), total 70 rations.

"The ponies should bring a further 15 boxes, which will give us 20 boxes = 200 rations. One guide will be staying with us, so that if we are still here until 9 Aug., i.e. another 30 days, we shall require 30 by 5 = 150 rations. This will leave us with

5 boxes over at the end, out of which the return journey of three days at 6 or perhaps 7 people will take a further 2 boxes. We are likely, therefore, to have carted 3 ration boxes too many up here. Since, however, we did not know at what speed we should go through them I consider this a perfectly prudent error.

" Very heavy rain this evening—much talk of whether the puffin or Wilson's petrel is the most numerous bird in the world. I persuaded Finnur to tell about the eiders again. He told us about a colony in Dýrafjörður at a farm called Mýrar, which is a new colony started during this century and built up by the farmer Gísli Vagusson (or perhaps more, Finnur thinks, by his wife). It now gives 50 kilos of down per year and must contain more than 3,000 pairs. Dýrafjörður is on the west side of the North-West Peninsula.

" Finnur thinks there are 400,000 eiders' nests in Iceland. He told again about his time on the island in Hrútafjörður, which was on a farm which belonged at that time to him. His grandfather actually built up an island for his eiders, which subsequently held 200 to 300 pairs.

" One delightful piece of eider behaviour which he described was a variant on the egg-covering habit. If the eider female was unable to cover her own eggs because the intruder advanced too fast, she would stop a little farther on and cover someone else's nest. This is a perfect example of an innate action serving a social purpose for which it can hardly have been evolved in the first place.

" In the evening we had the best radio contact yet. We ascertained that there were no messages for us and passed the position of our camp—' At Bólstaður on the west side of the River Þjórsá.' We asked him to pass this position to the British Minister. We felt well pleased, and I think James and Finnur felt reasonably well rewarded for all their efforts.

" *Tues. 10 July*. Another bright morning. I went into the marsh to catch Apus (*Lepidurus*), the primitive crustacean which looks like a tiny king-crab. One pool about four to six inches deep had a much greater number than any other, though there were a few of the creatures in one or two other pools. It seems that these pools must dry up in the later summer, but of course Apus can survive this. (Scientific name for Apus—*Lepidurus arcticus*.)

" I caught about fifty or sixty and filmed them in a bowl, together with a caddis-fly larva and some pond-snails—*Limnea ovata*. Afterwards I preserved the Apus in methylated spirit for Harold Munro Fox. Phil went down to the snow-bunting hide, now at eight feet from the nest-hole, and later we had a picnic lunch while sunbathing. We had thought of a plan for setting the net for half a dozen broods of pinkfeet which we could see through the heat haze on Oddkelsver, but by lunch-time they had moved down on to the sand and were washing in a pool. This spoiled the plan, for we had intended to creep along the sand and set the net below the brow, then drive them down off the marsh, with flankers to direct them.

In the afternoon the geese were still at the pool on the sand. I decided to go over the Blautakvísl in order to visit the swans' nest by which we had temporarily put the hide. From camp I had seen that she was off the nest. It was so warm and sunny when I left that I wore my rucksack over a bare top half.

" The geese saw me coming soon after I had crossed the river, and immediately started to go to the right towards the Þjórsá. I kept out as far as I could in order to head them off and went down quite suddenly in a quicksand, or rather quick gravel. It had a hard bottom about two feet down but it was unpleasant because so sudden. The interesting thing was that the geese seemed to recognise the security of the sands and the river, for they were not hurrying unduly. There were sixteen adults and either seven or eight broods. The important part was that a number of the parents were flightless. This is the first definite evidence we have had of flightless *parents*. The goslings with them must have been between two and three weeks old. Thus, supposing them to have hatched about 20 June, the first flightless non-breeders were seen about 3 July and the first flightless parents on 10 July.

" I climbed up the brow and could see, across the marsh, the swan sitting on her nest. As she was still sitting I decided not to disturb her, especially as a rain storm was creeping up the river. The sun had gone in, so I turned back. Two broods of geese which were up on the slope beyond the swan—about half a mile away—started to move off up the hill.

" On the way back I noticed a ringed plover running along the sand in front of me. He looked quite pretty against a pool, and I wondered if I should photograph him. I had just decided not to when he began to bathe in the pool, about fifteen yards away. I got out the camera and set it up on the tripod. The plover still bathed. I got out the big lens and fitted it to the camera. The plover had finished bathing but was preening charmingly. I estimated the range and set it on the lens, I got out the exposure meter and ascertained the light. The plover was preening away and looked delightful. I set the stop and put my eye to the view-finder. The plover flew away. So I took off the big lens, put the camera away and started on homeward again. Later I found a golden plover with a flock of about twenty-five dunlins in attendance —the largest flock I have seen so far. In such numbers it seems that the plover might be quite embarrassed.

" By this time a strong south wind had set in which was very cold. I put on all the clothes I had with me in my rucksack. The cold wind had completely banished the flies which had been troublesome early (although still only a small proportion bite). On the way back to camp I noticed an Opilionid (harvestman) carrying a small fly in its jaws. It was the long-legged species with the black mark down its back (*Mitopus morio*). The impending storm was behaving in a very strange way, for in England it would have been upon me in a few minutes driven by the stiff breeze. But here we have to get used to the idea of clouds forming and dispersing at certain given distances from the glaciers—or, at least, I suppose the glaciers to have some such influence. Anyway, the storm crept up the Þjórsá so slowly that, although we were equidistant from the camp when I turned back, I beat it home. Within two minutes of my return a great downpour came upon us. But our tents were waterproof and we were perfectly snug within. After the rain had passed—or stopped anyway—we began to discuss whether the ponies would arrive to-day. Finnur said that originally they had thought to *start* up on the 10th. I thought perhaps they would stick to that plan and perhaps be delayed a day, and maybe we should not expect them until 14th or 15th. At that precise moment we heard a sound. Swans, maybe. Finnur bobbed out of the tent. 'The horses are here'—and so they were. Three guides came, one of them Valentínus (Valli) Jónsson from Skaftholt, one called Ágúst Sveinsson from Ásar (the district postmaster) and one a fox-catcher, Fílippus Jónsson of Háholt. There were ten ponies in two trains. Ten minutes later they were being unloaded in a welter of ropes and straps and pack saddles.

It was a great event. We filmed and photographed it, and then we went into the tent to brew tea and to open the packages of mail and newspapers. Newspapers were the bulk of it, and a fat interesting-looking envelope on His Britannic Majesty's Service from the Minister contained only two lurid novelettes. There was nothing of interest from home, no news of the breeding successes, no news of the ducks from Mývatn—nothing but a tiresome detail for my Perry River book, and a boring letter from my lawyer. It is extraordinary how such a small thing can be so disappointing. Phil and I were quite crestfallen about it. James had several letters from his wife and Finnur one from his.

"The newspapers brought the world into our camp and the change was not for the better. True, there was to be an armistice in Korea, but the Persian oil dispute is not settled. We are in no way the better for being reminded of all these things and the periodicals threaten to waste a good deal of our precious time up here.

" In the evening we had a really successful radio communication with Gufunes, better even than last night. He heard us, strength two. We told him we had no messages for him but that our relief supplies had arrived by pony. (He couldn't get the word 'relief.') I gave him 'food supplies,' and he said: 'I understand your meat supplies, food supplies have arrived by pony.'

" If we can get as good communication to-morrow we propose to move the schedule time from 11.0 p.m. to 10.0. a.m.

" There were alarms and excursions because two of the ponies had started for home. Valli went after them and managed to get them back. He is to stay with us—with seven ponies—for the rest of the expedition."

CHAPTER VIII

James's Diary: The Goose-Pens

THE GUIDES made a lightning tour of the oasis on horseback the following day. Fílippus found the fox-earths blank and had no opportunity to lay his poisoned baits. When they came back on the evening of 11 July we decided to keep the base-camp where it was, as the grazing was good for the horses.

There was a marvellous sunset of mackerel sky, which turned to scarlet, and a strange vertical column of light appeared over the ice-cap. This was, no doubt, a reflection of the sun's track on the ice.

On the morning of 12 July Ágúst and Fílippus said goodbye and turned back for home, taking letters and newspaper dispatches from Peter and James. They cunningly led the horses upstream till out of sight round our headland, then doubled back along the river's edge. This was so as not to unsettle the seven ponies which are staying with us and which were feeding in the marsh.

These seven horses and the five people remaining had the oasis to themselves once again, this time for three weeks. At once we began to explore it all over again on horseback, led by Valli, who had a magnificent fast animal. Finnur had the same piebald horse, but the rest of us were freshly mounted. James had a much stronger animal, with a reputation for biting other horses. Phil's and Peter's were rather alike, with light tow-coloured manes, and Valli rode a magnificent bay with a coal-black mane and black edges to his ears. There were also two pack ponies, and, of course, they had to go everywhere with the rest.

In the early days Valli had a good deal of trouble preventing these animals from straying away down river, and on Friday, 13 July, an ill-omened date on which bad weather kept us in camp, he had a long chase after them lasting several hours, while the rest of us collected flowers in the marsh and tried not to worry. We found it a good deal easier to catch the goslings (and now the moulting adults too) with horses, though the last stages of the chase always involved dismounting and pursuing the birds on foot. It seemed that some more efficient method should be evolved and Peter was keen to use the 200 yards of rabbit-netting we had brought with us. On 14 July we set it in a V in the passage which crosses Oddkelsalda, across the lowest part. The place was carefully selected with high hopes, but when we tried to drive the geese from Oddkelsver we found that they ran up the hills, not towards passes or low places, but always for the very summit. So the drive was an almost comical failure. We re-set the nets later in the afternoon on a more promising hill-crest—the North Crest of Oddkelsalda was our name for it—and left them there so that we might make a catch there in a few days' time, although Peter's faith in the possibilities of these nets was slightly shaken, and the rest of the party was undisguisedly sceptical.

We heard on the radio that a British flying-boat was going to try to drop mail for us, but it had to return unexpectedly to Scotland with an ambulance case, and never came.

In spite of cold and windy weather the summer flowers of the tundra were bright and ever changing. The *Dryas* and thrift were over now, and new and no less beautiful ones were taking their place—the lovely almost orchid-like heads of deep pink alpine lychnis, *Viscaria alpina*, and the delicate and graceful grass of Parnassus, *Parnassia palustris*.

On 15 July James's diary runs :

" An excellent day ; though barometer low, it was overcast but warm and still until late evening, when a windy shower caught us. We spent 11.30-21.00 on a ride through Tjarnarver, across the Blautakvísl, to and up Nautalda, and back home through Oddkelsver. Started well ; startled a package of geese and goslings in creek north of " B " marsh, near river. Here I got within a foot of a goose crouching under the bank on the surface of a tarn but didn't have the guts to go into the water after it and lost it. A pretty bank here over this tarn, with two hatched pinkfoot nests we hadn't found before, as well as three old ones of previous years ; and on the same bank I found a ptarmigan's nest with six or seven hatched eggs, in a bush of *Salix lanata*. Finnur pointed out that the eggs were old, dry and stained, and therefore the brood was of a previous year. But proof that the ptarmigan *does* breed in the Þjórsárver.

" We next passed through Pintail Marsh and found that the swan whose nest we knew had hatched five cygnets safely, all of which we easily rounded up and marked ; much photography. The same pair of arctic terns was present ; made vicious attacks on Finnur. Continued north, and caught a good lot of geese and broods when crossing dry *Empetrum* and short-willow slope, and another goose from what we now call Ptarmigan Lake, a shallow lake, under a desert hill, into which Valli took his horse after it, getting off in mid-lake and actually catching it under water. How many would we catch without him ? Reason for the lake's title was a tame, very *brown* and white, small and thin (in comparison with Spitsbergen and Scottish ptarmigans) cock ptarmigan that ran about the lake edge on a bank in front of our horses but which, when Peter advanced with tripod, Kodachrome and long lens, flew croaking and burping away and indulged just out of camera-shot in soaring display-flight.

" We continued on, now in new country to us, and crossed the Blautakvísl just above its bifurcation that encloses the great island (not on map). This bifurcation separates at one of the big stony knolls that sit in the middle of these *vers* and not all of which, by any means, are marked on the map. The crossing approached by another knoll in Tjarnarver, and not at all difficult. After it a long crossing of upper Oddskelsver, over a tundra on which was no bird-life except dunlins and goldies and one pair of whimbrel, with three interposing black-sandy flats, one of which (the wildest) came at once after the crossing, and the other two of which (these are on the map) were evidently channels through which in times of flood the overflow of the Blautakvísl safety-valves off into the upper Miklakvísl. Nothing but trickles in these at the moment, and occasional sticky places in which our horses floundered a bit. Growing on the sandy flats, especially the first one, and in its first opening (flowers at bottom of the stem only) was the loveliest willow-herb I have ever seen, a glorious *Leander* colour (not quite cerise); a bilberry and cream colour and blossoms really very large, perhaps the largest open blossoms of the tundra. *Chamaenerion latifolium*, the Eyrarros, the " shingle-bank rose " of Iceland. An American species found in Europe only in Iceland. Also in Greenland. Peter had it on the Perry River. It is closely related to the British rose-bay willow-herb.

" Nautalda was a hospitable bluff with a green mossy meadow below it in which the horses grazed and tried to roll (until Valli stopped them) while we lunched. Lunch much interrupted by a chase after goslings (successful) and by a wagtail which caused us all trouble. Started with Phil saying : " What a yellow meadow-pipit," and me (*really* looking at a m.-p.) saying : " Just an ordinary one " (afterwards accused by Peter of birdsmanship ploy No. 1 for beginners). Then I really *did* see the yellow bird. It was a wagtail with bright sulphur-yellow underparts, greenish back tinge, and dark-slate head, with even darker cheeks. Its tail did not seem to be *particularly* long, and as it fed about the springs at this place it made chirps which Peter and I both thought very like those of *M. flava*. As it flew off some distance it got a bit of height and uttered a much louder, more penetrating and slightly more metallic chirp. Alternatives were one of the dark-headed forms of *M. flava*, a species never yet recorded in Iceland, and

Blue-headed Wagtail

M. cinerea, the grey wagtail, previously recorded twice in Iceland. Habitat suitable for either—a yellow wagtaily marsh and a grey wagtaily stream. White outer tail-feathers."

And here we must interrupt James's diary to point a moral. It continues (written down at the time) : " No doubt whatever, to Finnur and me, that was grey wagtail, especially after hearing voice." Which only goes to show how easy it is to come to the wrong conclusions, especially about what ought to be familiar animals, when they are encountered " out of their context." For our field notebooks by then carried enough notes to make it clear that it was, in fact, a yellow wagtail—*Motacilla flava*. But we had (or James had) jumped to conclusions based on voice, which in any case is an unreliable character among wagtails (at least, normal alarm-note is so); and on second thoughts about length of tail as the bird flew across a stream. (The grey wagtail's tail is markedly longer in proportion to its body than that of the *flava* wagtails.) Second thoughts were wrong: the greenish back, the absence of yellow rump, the dark cheeks, are the characters which established it unquestionably as *flava*, when we looked at our field-books again. But James had a bad day with the wagtail, starting with a crude (albeit unconscious) birdsmanship gambit[1], and ending with an elementary hash-up of elementary note-taking drill.[2] Back to James's diary at Nautalda:

"The stream here was a remarkable one, flowing through sunk mossy banks from a dozen springs, some quite large, and most rising in great mossy holes in the ground, some ten feet deep, gurgling out at the bottom of these holes and then running underground again a few yards to reappear in another hole or in a deep channel. Finnur disappeared entirely down one such hole, botanising—the lips of them and sides of the depressions were rich natural gardens in which prominent elements, besides mosses, were cranesbill, *Archangelica*, *Potentilla*, buttercup. Finnur found three new plants—*Epilobium alsinifolium*, *Cerastium cerastoides*, *Phleum alpinum*. Also the very pale *Viola palustris*, and *Pyrola minor*, and much *Saxifraga stellaris*, very large, and *S. cernua*.

"Peter found a gosling cheeping in one of these holes. It could not get out. When we ringed and released it it did not go far away, but grazed hungrily on the pretty bank of the

[1] See Campbell, B. (1951). Birdsmanship. *Bird Notes*, 25: 33-37 (35); and in Potter, S. (1952). *One-upmanship*, London and Yeovil, Hart-Davis, 109-15 (112). These references have been kindly brought to the attention of the members of the expedition by the other members of the expedition, *ad nauseam*.

[2] This is James's chapter and the foregoing paragraph of self-abasement was, of course, written by him. P.S.

stream; Peter thought it must have been so hungry because it had been in the hole for several days.

"As we left this fine lunch-place we found the remains of an adult pinkfoot in a great splash of feathers on the ground. Among the pinkfoot feathers was a brown one which Peter picked up; it certainly was not of pinkfoot—a great body or flank feather which could only belong to a white-tailed eagle, though we took the feather along with us for checking at the Museum.

"After lunch some goslings took us on an uphill chase up Nautalda, and we arrived soon at the top, from which we had a fine view of the inner marshes between us and the ice-cap. Many geese, perhaps nearly a hundred including broods, saw us and made off the marsh (though 1½ kilometres away) on to the grey barren foothills of Soðulfell. We would not have had time to interview them, anyway. Valli on his sure-footed bay dashed about the tops of Nautalda and eventually found for us one of the goose-pens which I photographed from every angle. Dimensions 12 by 2 metres (Pl. 8, p. 81).

"There can be no doubt that these are goose-pens, and made many hundreds of years ago. The interior of the one on the south side of Nautalda (near the top) has silted up, which has preserved the back wall from collapsing as have those of the sides. These have fallen over westwards. All walls were made of boulders just small enough for a strong man to carry, and were dry-stone. The pen was very cunningly sited about three-quarters way up Nautalda on a flat above a slightly convex slope, so that the geese going uphill would not see it until the last moment, and so that the human operators should have cover."

There is only one reference in the rather lengthy literature of Iceland to the use of these pens. In 1638, the last year of his life, Gísli Oddsson, the Bishop of Skálholt in South Iceland, wrote a treatise on the natural phenomena of Iceland in his native tongue. The original is lost, but a Latin treatise, *De Mirabilibus Islandiae*, by Ketill Jörundsson, one of his ministers, is in Bodley's Library in Oxford. This is what Gísli says:

> " I speak of fowl which come from abroad; throughout the winter these do not dwell among us and are not even observed. Such are commonly the wild geese, the *graagaaser*, so called from their ashy colour. These are somewhat smaller than swans, and in spring-time they occupy the island in an almost countless number; in winter, however, they are nowhere to be seen. The common report is that every year in autumn they make for the neighbouring countries of England, Ireland [he writes *Hiberniam, Irlandiam*] and Scotland and in spring leave those countries and wait upon us. I must put on record the most remarkable usefulness of these birds. By the generosity of Providence they provide for us, and leave bountifully [he writes *like loot*] exceedingly tasty eggs, their own flesh to feed on and feathers to use. Our bird-catchers keep a careful look-out for the time (which appears miraculous) when the young geese, half-grown, and exceedingly fat, and living for the most part in deserted places, have not yet become able to fly—the time when their parents are also unable to fly, having no strength left, and their wing-feathers being moulted [*sucked down to the blood*]. Then, I say, our hunters are at hand; they prepare beforehand fixed fences, mounds or pens whither with no trouble they drive the flocks of birds like sheep to the slaughter; when they are shut up they then kill all they choose, since the geese have no chance left to them of escaping by the help of their wings."

These statements are in many respects remarkable, since they show that the catching of the flightless geese in these pens, in the interior, went on up to the seventeenth century; most people had thought that with the close of the Saga Age, in the fourteenth and fifteenth centuries, the Icelanders had given up going into the interior altogether. But certainly there is no evidence that they went there in the eighteenth century or early nineteenth, and all the old interior crossings had to be rediscovered in the last hundred and forty years. Gísli's statement that the geese of Iceland are wintering in the British Isles is also remarkable, when we consider the ideas then prevalent about bird migration.

James's diary continues :

" When we descended from the pens (down the slope up which the geese were presumably driven), we found at the bottom of the hill a patch of *Saxifraga oppositifolia* in full flower. Unfortunately, I could not photograph the *Silene*-coloured, mauve-pink flowers in colour, as I'd run out of colour film, but tried instead black and white. Peter and Finnur thought that this patch had been lately covered with snow—hence so late.

" We aimed towards Oddkelsalda across the flat, boggier part of Oddkelsver. After a little we were riding on firmish ridges along the right bank of the Miklakvísl, and found the only sign of goose-nests in this area, two traditional sites on firm mounds. A pair of whimbrels, and a few pairs of goldies and dunlins. We approached perhaps a little too near Oddkelsalda for Peter's liking (because of disturbing geese near the net which we had left), but branched off towards the Blautakvísl crossing and the hill of 627 metres at a place probably corresponding to hill 609 metres on the map, but bearing no resemblance to it on the ground. Here were many tarns and hillocks, and two largish tarns or small lakes. Name, Foxwarren, for in one of the little hillocks were four or five holes, with worn-smooth approaches and a litter of goose and lamb bones around ; but no fresh foxprints. The hunters had cleared this earth last year, and it had not yet been recolonised.

" Foxwarren was one of the alternative camping-sites that had been considered for us ; there was good water in the lakes, fine grazing ground for the horses, and a dry sward for the tents. Around the foxholes there was a great growth of cranesbill, *Armeria* and *Potentilla* and in the grazing meadow many buttercups and dandelions. A sharp misty shower of rain drove us into our mackintoshes, but we saw a red-throated diver at close quarters in a long lochan (it flew away after a dive in the opposite direction to that in which it flew, and pattered for over 100 metres before taking off down-wind). We also saw a duck scaup on one of the lakes, and on the other a dozen or more phalaropes, some already coming out of plumage, and two broods of tiny new-hatched baby long-tailed ducks (7 and 4), the smaller of which was accompanied by three adults, the larger by none. Our first formal proof of the breeding of this species in the Þjórsárver.

" As we skirted the south side of 627 metres on our way home we came across a freshly-killed gosling. Its head was about 3 metres from its body, which had been much eaten (breast and intestines). We thought, an Iceland falcon, probably, and later events showed this to be likely. Indeed, we may have pushed it off the kill, as it was not finished.

" In sight of camp. The horses (mine particularly) showed much more enthusiasm about trotting, and when we saw a brood of goslings with parents in sight of the Blautakvísl it was not difficult to persuade mine to break into a canter, over some fairly uneven ground. While this took place my saddle described a simple rotatory movement and I caused much amusement to Peter, following hard behind, in my efforts to jerk it backward and remain in it. However, by the time I could stay on no longer it was necessary to get off, anyway, to catch a gosling! Valli jumped into a tarn up to his waist to catch one of the adults.

" As we were catching these geese the Iceland falcon appeared, and circled round. Again, I had a very definite impression of slowness. Wing-beats very slow compared with those of peregrine. But probable the actual airspeed rather high, and much higher than it looks. A darkish bird, probably the same one as we had seen with a gosling yesterday. Finnur saw it kill another about 200 metres from us—not outright as it struggled on the ground for a bit.

"We aimed not for the delta crossing, but straight for camp to where the Blautakvísl was single, and Valli went on ahead on his own horse, towing the two pack-animals. They splashed in, and he was soon up to his knees and his horse nearly swimming. So he came back and we all floundered along the muddy bank down to the delta crossing; at least all but Fisher, for coming last, my horse picked its own way along a mossy bank of the main river-stream very near the edge. This was fine until it got bogged in the moss and began to flounder. It became clear to me presently that this floundering was considerable and rather out of control, and I rolled off it to the left (i.e. still on the bank) just as it slid into the river on the right. It then waded out to midstream, which was half-way up its saddle, and started to walk down-river to the Þjórsá, in which Valli told us afterwards he thought it was going to end. The others found a certain bizarre element in the situation, overtaken as they were by a riderless horse in midstream. However, the mare soon thought better of its first idea and after about 100 metres in midstream waded ashore to Valli's horse, and he brought it back to me. I got on my wet saddle, and we all easily forded the delta and got back to camp. Valli was the only one really in need of dry clothes."

Snowy Owl
looking backwards

CHAPTER IX

Goose-netting: and a Snowy Owl

PETER'S DIARY for the next days runs:

"*Mon. 16 July.* The plane is due to drop mail, perhaps films, perhaps cigarettes to-day. Visibility was not good early on, but it has greatly improved this afternoon. It is now 4.20 p.m. and no plane has arrived. There seems no reason why it should not come now, however, although it has clouded over slightly. Our hopes were raised early this morning when we heard a plane, but it was the Catalina going to Seyðisfjörður and later in the day we heard it coming back.

"Phil spent the morning cooking some of the edible lichen (which has to be boiled in milk—condensed in our case—for two hours). It was rather bitter at first, but with rice, sugar and raisins added it was quite good, if a bit gooey. A little bacon with it was rather tasty. The lichen is called *fjällagræs*, *Tetraria islandica*.

"James has been collecting blackflies, gnats, etc., from the tent roof, and Finnur is skinning two large goslings, one accidentally killed by the ponies and the other by the Iceland falcon.

" We are all a bit restive at wasting a day of potential goose-catching, but it does us no harm to get our notes up to date and take time off for such things as insect collecting. All the same, I hope the plane comes to-day, because it will be a bore wasting a second day waiting around for it.

" But the plane didn't come. We spent a rather frustrating day collecting invertebrate life round the camp. James caught a number of interesting flies including a wasp or Hymenopteran of some kind, a hover fly, *Syrphus* sp., some moths (Geometers). We have also found a very numerous green larva feeding on *Salix glauca*.[1] I made a plankton net out of a handkerchief and later an improved one out of a dishcloth, and caught great numbers of copepods and cladocerans, and what appears to be a tiny insect of the water-boatman type, but very minute. The larva of a *Dytiscus*-type water-beetle was another specimen. One of the most striking things was the way in which the little crustaceans turned brilliant orange the instant they were put into spirit. The change was almost instantaneous. James found a meadow-pipit's nest, and caught the female in his butterfly net.

" The snow-buntings are not yet fledged, but getting quite big in the nest, with lemon-yellow gapes.

" Not only was there no plane, but no message about its non-arrival on the radio, leaving us completely in the air. He could not read us and rang off almost at once.

" *Tues. 17 July*. We gave the plane till noon to come, but it was not a very hopeful day, with cloud and rain showers hanging round Kerlingarfjöll. At 12.30 p.m. we set off across the Blautakvísl in order to drive geese into the nets on

[1] This is what the snow-buntings (p. 81) were feeding on. It turned out to be a sawfly larva.

Oddkelsalda. Once over the river (at 12.50 p.m.) we divided, agreeing to reach the net in an hour. This was on the short side, and Phil and I regretted it as we came to the western entrance to the Barnacle Marsh, because sitting under a little cliff of tundra was a huge white bird—a snowy owl! Some geese-broods which were running away from us would not run past it, but branched off and up a hill. The owl was so placed that, had we had the time, we could have stalked up quite close to it.

" As it was, the closest view we had of it was about 300 yards. It looked quite white and was therefore probably an old male. Its white-feathered legs were very prominent. At 250 yards it flew, flopping over the hill, with about the same speed of wing-flap as a swan. For a while it flew just below the ridge, so that only the tips of its wings on the up-strokes were visible.

" Near the Foxwarren we came on another bunch of geese. It had begun to rain—a heavy shower—and Phil stopped to put on waterproof trousers. I rode slowly up the ridge, and when I looked over, there were the geese, perhaps forty to fifty of them, old and young, in the middle of a large pool. Had the whole party been there I am convinced that we could have surrounded the lake before they got to the shore, and kept them in the middle while we rigged nets.

" As we approached the north crest of Oddkelsalda and our nets, Phil shouted that she could see geese down at the edge of the Miklakvísl. They were already retiring, evidently from the approach of Valli from the other side. Some were crossing the river, but at the same time we saw others on top of our hill and almost within the arms of our net.

" Phil and I climbed slowly and as I came to the saddle I saw that Finnur and James were still far out on the marsh beyond. A ptarmigan flew across and settled 200 yards away, only the second we have seen up here. Looking to the left I saw Valli coming up the slope driving an adult and two goslings ahead of him. I was directly between them and the net. There was a cliff at the edge of the *Salix* sward, and I rode under it and waited motionless. But the goose saw me and turned off. Valli saw this and managed to turn it back before the net. Meanwhile Phil saw a gosling crouching and came over towards me. This was the signal for some adults to sneak out round her wing of the net. She went back in time to pick up one crouching bird, and I advanced over the crest. About a dozen birds were going forward into the cage. One adult got tangled in the rabbit nets, and nearer the cage another adult and a gosling were caught up. Otherwise the birds had gone into the cage without a hitch. This catch—fifteen in all—was rather a triumph, although it was a sad pity that so many had got across the Miklakvísl. On the other hand, a very large catch might well have produced something of a shambles in the cage. It is evident that several cages would be an improvement.

" We released one pair of geese soon after a group of goslings, and as soon as the adults were over the first ridge they slowed down and waited for the goslings. By the time they reached the second ridge they were all in company, except for one smaller gosling which had got left behind. This is the first time we have seen adults which we have handled pay any real attention to goslings.

" Having ringed and released the rest of the birds we decided to leave the nets for a later catch, and to ride on into Illaver and Arnarfellsver. The weather was improving, we had already done well and we went down to the crossing of the Miklakvísl—the big stream—in high spirits.

" We found an empty hatched pinkfoot nest in Illaver on the bank of Miklakvísl and had lunch not far from our lunch-place on the day we went to the moraine. We hoped to find geese round the small wave in Illaver, which we have named Illaversalda and which was where we saw the pink-bottomed goose on the return journey from the moraine. There were no geese, but near the summit Finnur sighted a pile of stones which he thought might be another goose-fold. When it was clear that there were no geese round the wave we rode back to the stones, and found, sure enough, that it was a goose-fold. It was a good deal smaller than the one of Nautalda. It was about six metres long and two wide but appeared to have been rather narrower at the entrance. The structure was razed to the ground, and it looked as though someone had later used the stones to make a cairn. But the shape of the fold could be seen fairly clearly from the row of half-buried stones which must have formed the base of the original wall.

" At the foot of Arnarfellsalda is a large nameless lake. It is actually the largest lake in the whole of Þjórsárver—about 500 yards long. We have christened it Lake Valli or Vallarvatn. On this lake we could see a crowd of geese swimming—some of them even upending.

" By the time we had crossed the two Múlakvísls, Fremri Múlakvísl and Innri Múlakvísl—in southern Iceland they do not use *north* and *south* but distinguish between outer or seaward (*Fram*, adjective *Fremri*) and inner (*Inn*, *Innri*), but in the north *Fram* means " towards the mountains," so the word must have come to mean *south*—the geese had all gone off the lake, and we saw the last of them topping the crest of Arnarfellsalda, the stony hill above. We went round the foot of this large wave to its eastern side facing Þjórsá (finding two empty hatched pinkfoot nests on the way), and rounding the shoulder of the hill found some geese and set off to hunt. The hunt led James, Finnur and me to the top of the ridge, James on foot and somewhat exhausted. Valli careered about the marsh below, in which there were some very small young and a brave and solicitous pair of adults which refused to leave the area. There was also a worried whimbrel and a black-backed gull. The results of this hunt were poor—three goslings and one adult female. The female who had stayed behind bravely and been caught as a result paid no attention to the goslings (which were undoubtedly hers) and ran off in a different direction. On the other hand the flying gander in the marsh was much concerned about the peeping goslings and flew up to the top of the wave whither they had scuttled.

" Ahead of us as we rode on was a pair of whooper swans with five cygnets. We started off to go to them, but Finnur saw some geese far up the hill on our left and he and Valli set off in pursuit. The rest of us thought they were much too far and shouted to call off the hunt; but the shout wasn't heard, so we said we had better go and help—better finish it now it's started. The chance seemed pretty poor.

" But when we reached the top of the hill we found that there were geese crouching and trying to sneak away everywhere. This was because Finnur and Valli had almost encircled them, and there must have been a great crowd—perhaps sixty geese—up there.

" After half an hour we gradually reassembled with the sacks well filled.

" We finally ringed and released twenty-three geese from this hunt, including six adults. Phil caught three of these adults. One gosling I was chasing seemed to regard me (on my horse) as a fellow escapee. When I got ahead of it, it ran on towards me. When I slowed down it slowed down, and when I stopped it stopped and stood below looking up at me in the most delightful way.

" By the time we had finished the ringing the swans and their five cygnets had reached the Þjórsá, and we saw another pen with two cygnets, but if we were to get back for our radio sked and learn what had happened to the aircraft, we thought we should start home. Before starting we looked NE across Arnarfellsver with the glasses and saw a great crowd of geese spread out across the flat marshes. They were everywhere, bunched and scattered, feeding in the green patches, standing along the edges of the Þjórsá tributaries which run down through the bog. There must have been fully five hundred adult geese in that part of the marsh, the nearest still drawing away from us, although already about a mile away.

"We wondered whether later it might not be possible to herd this great concourse back on to Arnarfellsalda and into our nets.

"We rode back along the west side of the wave and came upon a gosling, clearly a part of our hunt, which brought its total to twenty-four.

"On the lake—Vallarvatn—there were several broods swimming away, some with parents, some without. There were also a barren pair of swans and two pairs of long-tailed ducks.

"As we came to the outfall of the lake we saw four large goslings coming towards us. We led them away from the water, and then Valli went round and herded them while I called them on, and filmed them as they came. When they were ten yards away they branched off and the chase was on. It took a deal of running to get all four. When they'd been ringed and released it looked as though another bunch of about nine goslings would come up to us. For a bit they swam towards us, but in due course they seemed to realise we were not what they were looking for and swam out again.

"We rode home quite fast, without any adventures until we came to the crossing of Blautakvísl. Here, at the point of Oddkelsver, were about three or four families of geese and they began to cross the river. A great hunt ensued on the sand, and in the river itself. At one time Valli was riding down the deepest part of the stream with his pony half submerged, chasing a diving gosling. When he finally caught it on the far bank I could see, from 40 yards away, the glint of a tag on its wing. It transpired that Phil had also caught a tagged one and released it (C535).

"At the close of the hunt we had two adults and two young (one a recap) plus Phil's recap—a catch of five.

"On the way back across Blautakvísl Phil's horse fell in midstream and pitched her into the water. This was rather disastrous as her camera and glasses were totally submerged. She came ashore dripping but still holding the bag with the two goslings in it. She was soaked, of course, but otherwise, thank God, quite unhurt.

" We took the catch back to camp (where I made the sad discovery that I had lost my nice little pliers—I think near Vallarvatn). James got out his balance (spring) and weighed the birds. The adults seemed to be a pair and weighed ♂ 6 lbs., ♀ 5½ lbs., to the nearest quarter pound.

We ringed the tagged recap (C. 537) with No. 21108 and weighed him—2¼ lbs. He was estimated to be 5-6 days old on 2 July, thus he was about 20-21 days. This is the size of gosling I have been putting down as four weeks, so it is most useful to be able to apply this correction. This bird is average of the larger goslings and indicates that 26 June—the date of our arrival—was perhaps the peak hatching-date of the season.

" So we were home in good time for the radio (which we have changed to 10.0 p.m. from 11.0) after yet another marvellous day, with a record catch of fifty geese marked plus two recaps (sixteen adults).

" After hastening home to be in time for the radio, Gufunes was half an hour late in calling. But when he did come up he heard us fairly well. He passed a message from the British Minister handed in at 16.38 saying :

' *Aircraft delayed. Hope arriving tomorrow.*'

This was ambiguous to the extent that we wondered whether the aircraft was arriving *chez nous* to-morrow, or just arriving in Reykjavík.

" We sent back :

' *Please give time of dropping. Instruct him to drop even if no one seen at camp.*'

He could not get " seen " and finally took the message as :

' *Please give time of dropping. Instruct to drop even if no one being at camp.*'

We thought this good enough, and arranged a schedule for 10.0 a.m. to-morrow."

Gufunes called at 10.0 on 18 July, but was very weak and could not hear us, though the operator could hear that we answered. He said we should try again at 12.0 noon. If he had had a message about the plane, we thought, he would surely have broadcast it. The glass was shooting up and the day was windless with thin cloud, which looked as if it would burn up and turn it into a very hot day. There were already a good many flies. We were all tired of waiting for the aircraft; we were hoping for cigarettes and mail, but Peter most of all for film.

We set off at about 1.0 p.m., intending to go up Tjarnarver to Nautalda, and perhaps to Nauthagi. But the high grey cloud thickened from the south-west and turned, after about two hours, to rain.

We rode up the now familiar edge of Tjarnarver, finding one or two new empty hatched goose nests, and the remains of an arctic fox lying near the remains of the poisoned sheep that had killed it. James had located a goose-fold on top of the hill to the north-west of the camp and quite close to it; evidently these folds were fairly common.

The most noticeable feature of the outward journey was the lack of geese. There were one or two families far out in the marsh, but it was quite different, even, from the last visit. Just before Ptarmigan Lake, before the rain had got under way, we decided to have lunch, once across the next ridge. On the ridge was another goose-fold, not recorded by Jóhann (who had given Finnur a list of nine known to him). This one was in rather better repair than the one in Illaver. The walls at the closed end were still two feet high; the structure was eight metres long and, as before, about two metres wide. The site was good—on a grey gravelly ridge, just over the crest.

We lunched on a rocky knoll, where there was an old

disused fox's earth, and an empty hatched goose nest. Over the very next ridge, after lunch, we came upon a party of geese down in the outfall of Ptarmigan Lake. They ran up the hill behind in the pouring rain, and the hunt was on. One party of about twelve very large goslings ran off to the left and as Peter drew level with them they crouched. There on the moss in front of him were these twelve goslings—he could see every one. James came over to help. But as fast as Peter walked up to each, fast or slow, obvious or stealthy, up it jumped and ran off. Eventually James and Peter caught one each. Up the hill Phil had caught one adult. Finnur had had trouble with his horse. He came disconsolately down the slope to Peter and explained that the animal had refused to go on, with two adults just ahead. Either he would have to have a different horse, or he would have to stay behind and the others would go on.

As they were talking, three goslings came over the hill with Valli in pursuit. One crouched and he caught it. Peter went away after another, cantering over the crest of the hill, and following it down the other side into a little hollow with a tarn and a snowdrift. Before getting to the water the gosling crouched and presently Peter saw another crouched there. The first was exhausted and was caught without difficulty, for he never moved; the second, however, jumped up and set off up the very steep hill. For fifty yards Peter tried to follow, hoping the hill might be steep enough to slow him up, but it wasn't, so he went back to his horse, which decided to start up the hill long before he was properly mounted. The next moment Valli appeared over the top where Peter had last seen his gosling. He pointed back the way it had gone and the two of them climbed together, but there was no sign of the bird. It must have crouched. Peter tried back, and there it was like a great moss-covered boulder—these three-week goslings are great big birds. Valli picked it up after a short sharp chase downhill. Downhill seemed to be the way to chase goslings, for they stumbled and then crouched. James, still on top of the hill, had found another goose-fold; this was the fifth they had seen, three of them apparently unknown until then.

Valli and Peter rode back and then we tried out a new clearance technique. James picked each bird out of the sack, Phil handed Peter the rings, Peter ringed (and crimped the clip) and Finnur wrote down. In this way we got through the six goslings and four adults far more quickly than before, and with much less mess and trouble. The whole operation was done standing—again easier, especially in heavy rain.

Valli had put down his whip somewhere, and after hearing of Finnur's difficulty with his skewbald, went off on him to look for it. The big pony was almost as reluctant again, although eventually Valli returned with his whip.

He announced then that the horses needed a day's rest. He was ready to go to Nautalda or Nauthagi that day but he felt the horses should have the day off on the next. This goose-hunting was harder work than bringing up the supplies from Ásólfsstaðir.

But the rain was heavy and cold, and the prospect of catching many geese not good. We decided to turn back, and headed southward across a part of the desert in order to cover a new track on the way back.

Only one adventure befell us on that chilly ride home. The hills were rocky and bare, with sparse vegetation in occasionally small bogs, which were very soft to cross. On a hill about half a mile away Phil spotted a white object. It was the snowy owl.

As James had not seen this bird on the day before, or indeed ever before in the wild state, his diary describes the rest of the day.

"Here came the rectification of yesterday's disappointments, for Phil saw the snowy owl standing on a cairn, on a grey hill not far from the Tjarnarver-Hnífá oasis-salient, and we were soon wresting our field-glasses from our bosoms and trying to get a good look before they wetted up. Which I did, to my great joy—a new bird for my life-tally. Phil seemed almost cross that I should get such joy out of a relatively distant view of a new bird. But it was not so distant as all that; and anyway the whole point is the *setting*. To have seen the snowy owl in its *own* area, in its hunting beat; to know through the evidence of one's own eyes that it is a part of the animal community, one of the small band of predators that skims a crop off this unique assembly of geese, which gives this set of *vers* an unparalleled character.

"Peter made some sketches of the owl, and would have got a cinetelephoto shot of it had the owl obeyed studio instructions,

Snowy Owl

and not mist-appeared (little boy's version of "mysteriously disappeared" now in S.W.T. usage). But we saw it beautifully fly from its cairn to another rock on the top of another grey hill. It had some speckles on its back, not many. Was probably an old male, and *very* probably the same one as Peter and Phil had seen on the previous day. As it sat on its cairn its back was towards us, but, owl-like, it had watched us, head turned 180°. In flight bulky body, short tail, round—and flight, as Peter says, whooper-tempo wing-beats, and then a long flat glide to a new sitting-place. Impression of complete command and ownership of the situation and site. Seen well through glasses at 200 m.

"Returned happy to camp to noise of red-throats; Finnur reported snow-buntings still in nest. Made hand-nets for catching goslings. Phil a bit cold and low. I wash up."

There were showers of drizzle during the night and in the early morning of 19 July. At 10.00 there was a message which did not come through very well; it said that the British Minister was still awaiting news of the aircraft and would let us know.

In the afternoon it brightened up, and Peter, Phil and James went for a walk. Finnur went down to the *kofi* to blow eggs; following him down, we saw the baby snow-buntings almost fledged in the nest, three of them; the gapes of their bills were yellow and strangely kinked, and there were still stray downy tufts on their heads. The male was seen in attendance.

We collected puffballs for supper, and Phil picked *Viscaria alpina* and *Chamaenerion latifolium* (the shingle rose) for a table decoration. James found an empty hatched pinkfoot nest on top of the *kofi*. We had lately begun to worry in case some of the nests we had recorded were not of the current year; after much deliberation we decided this particular one could not be older.

On the way to the red-throated diver lake, on a small stony hill, we found another goose-fold, our sixth. This was a very primitive one, quite small (five metres long), using a large rock as part of the wall. It was not easy to see where the entrance had been.

On the lake below we saw an adult diver landing; one young one came out to meet it and was fed. As we arrived at the pool the male went off in a flurry patter—there was no wind. It returned in about twenty minutes with a fish, a little shorter than the red-throat's bill, thinnish and round, dark on the back, very light on the belly. Finnur said the Iceland sticklebacks were not as big as this, but later, at Nauthagi and elsewhere, we saw sticklebacks as big.

We made our way over towards the river, past a part of the tundra with the best patches of the brilliant yellow *Saxifraga hirculus* we had yet seen. As we came to the Þjórsá a big crowd of geese ran into the river and set off to swim across. Peter filmed them as they swam, all in a tight bunch, just as the snow-geese do in Canada. They came to an island of sand, scuttled across it and swam on towards the far bank. Once ashore some were ready to dally, but one or two birds must have been urgent, and away the little flock went. As they climbed the bank beyond it could be seen that there were twenty-six adults, eleven goslings; this was rather a new proportion. None of them was ringed. At the top of the ridge they paused before they disappeared over it. Over on Sóleyjarhöfði was a smaller bunch of geese moving slowly up the hill. They did not seem to have spotted us.

On the way back we found another hatched and empty nest along the river-bank, beside a cairn marking the path. The lovely delicate greenish-white *Parnassia palustris* was beginning to flower in profusion, taking the place of the *Dryas*; the *Parnassia* buds are like pale green pinheads and look delightful.

Phil cooked a splendid risotto when we got back to camp—with chopped puffballs to flavour the rice, bacon and peas; this helped to make up for the disappointment when there was no call from Gufunes. Finnur trimmed his ginger moustache with a blunt pair of scissors.

Red-throated Diver

CHAPTER X

Peter's Diary: The Flowers of the Eagle's Fell

"*Fri. 20 July.* Windless with high overcast. Rather a warm day, and the flies a nuisance. No joy with a long shot at the radio at 10.0 a.m. We had made no 'sked', but they say they are keeping continuous watch on that wave. It is evidently vastly more difficult to communicate during the day.

"We spent the morning packing up our sleeping tents and night requirements for a three-day trip, and, as I write, Valli is saddling and loading the ponies. With James's new hand-nets we shall look more than ever like a band of White Knights. Finnur has been down to the *kofi* to get his plant-collecting equipment. He reports that the first baby snow-bunting has left the nest. The day improves as we set off—to work the nets at Oddkelsalda, and on to Arnarfell.

"And a splendid day, too. At 1.30 we set out across the Blautakvísl and went straight towards the Foxwarren. As we came to the gap west of the Barnacle Marsh, Valli skilfully noticed geese ahead. There was a little ridge about 200 yards away. As we galloped over it there came into view a great bunch of geese—I thought about 100—and Valli and Phil were on top of them. I went out to the left and caught an adult and three young. Phil caught no less than five adults.

James, who, because he has a slow pony, now takes charge of the pack-horses, caught three goslings which had broken back, and after just under an hour we had ringed and released our record catch—twenty-eight geese, of which thirteen were adults.

" One of the main features of this success was the new hand-nets which James had made from the uprights of the photographic hides with a wire hoop and a loose piece of string netting. They were admirably useful.

" As we rode on we passed the lake where the long-tailed ducks had young. We saw the brood of three.

" The drive to the nets was conducted by an approach from one side only this time. Valli was to gallop round the point along the Miklakvísl bank and out across the marsh. In this plan much depended on where the geese were in the marsh, and, as it happened, they were well away from our hill and headed, as soon as they saw Valli, for the main mass of Oddkelsalda. A few turned and ran up the hill, and some went on to the lake. I saw some on the hill-top and went round the lake. I came upon an adult crouching under the bank. I tried to use the net, crept up, but the goose had lifted his head and flapped out, just as I lunged. I tripped, fell headlong on the bank at the very brink of the lake.

" One goose I had seen against the outside of the net. Valli went up and caught it, and perhaps a second, and then withdrew again. On my way up the hill I started a crouching adult, but it gained on my reluctant pony and therefore would not crouch.

" When I reached the top the others had got the geese into bags. There were six adults, which ultimately turned out all to be males, and four goslings. One adult had approached the net from the wrong side and got tangled.

" Although we had ten geese it was a sad disappointment. Had we done the drive as we did the last time we should surely have had sixty at least.

"We lunched after the Miklakvísl crossing. Thirty-eight geese before lunch was good, even if lunch was at 5.0 p.m. The flies were very troublesome as it was windless and rather heavy. Thin high cloud had gradually obscured the sun. Rain seemed imminent but who could say how imminent.

"It was not until we had crossed both the Fremri and Innri Múlakvísls that we came to more geese—this time two unaccompanied goslings on a lake, which were finally caught after Valli had plunged in and was wading above his knees. A single gosling was peeping out on the sand at the edge of the Þjórsá but it would not come to us.

"Last time we had been at Vallarvatn I had left my nice spring pliers behind. We hunted for them now, and James found them—the clue being a piece of string, from a bunch of rings which had been exhausted on the four goslings we caught at this spot. I was greatly delighted at the recovery of these pliers, which I secured to my belt by the piece of string in question. Part of the reason for my pleasure was that these pliers are the best for ringing and do the job much quicker than the ones I had been using since the loss; part also, no doubt, was the rectifying of the untidiness of losing them; but a large part also was related to the loss of a toy and came from long ago.

"When Finnur came up he had found a dunlin sitting on two rotten eggs, one cracked and the other, which, when tested, floated the wrong way up.

"We repeated the route of our last visit to Arnarfellsalda, going round the eastern side. Once more we found the swan with the five cygnets, once more we set out to catch and tag them, once more as we approached them we sighted geese near the top of Arnarfellsalda, and once more we left the swans to go after the geese. This time it may have been a mistake, for although, after a chase all over the top and down the other side, we caught two adults and three goslings, yet I think this could still have been achieved after tagging the swans.

" The goose chase led down past a lake with a brood of three longtails to the Innri Múlakvísl, and there Valli and Phil surprised the white-tailed eagle at a gosling which he had just killed and which was evidently one of the brood we had disturbed. The eagle had evidently caught the gosling in the water as it was soaking wet. Phil saw it rise out of the water. The bird flopped across to a mound on the other side of the river, where it sat, being mobbed by a whimbrel. We crossed the river, but when I dismounted in order to film him, the eagle flopped off, turned and flopped past us, to settle across the river behind us. We found and photographed the gosling —headless, but still quite warm. Valli led me on my horse back across the river for another effort to film the eagle, which was a complete failure. He flew at 150 yards, and when I put on my rucksack the winder of my watch broke off. Valli and I looked for it, but a hopeless search. We marked the place with a feather, but we shall never have a chance to look for it, I expect.

" We had seen about twenty unaccompanied goslings in the marsh ahead of us, and in due course we came up with them. Eight of them came towards us—to within about 100 yards— after which they started off away from us and we in pursuit. So began one of the most arduous and least rewarding hunts we have undertaken.

" Early in the hunt six goslings crouched in a bunch. Phil and I crept to within two or three yards, then up they sprang and ran in all directions. Valli chased up four more, and for a while we were running in all directions over soft mossy bog with occasional harder mounds of tundra. Sometimes in these mounds there would be a sudden subsidence as the ice cracked and broke below the moss. The bog was so soft in places that poor Phil went right through and fell forward, getting soaked to the skin, and wetting her camera again (the other camera this time).

" Without James's new nets we should never have caught

any. As it was we caught three before the area was clear except for four in a lochan. Valli plunged into this and for half an hour waded about almost up to his middle. The goslings dived hopelessly and Valli, in that depth of water, was insufficiently mobile. At last he caught one, and in due course the other three crept ashore, to be caught, one by Finnur, one by Phil and one by me.

"This brought our total to fifty-two—equal to the catch on 17 July.

"By this time it was almost 9.0 p.m. and we had but a short stretch of marsh to cross to reach the outer moraine. Here we decided to make camp beside a mossbound spring, in the lee of the steep richly flowered bank.

"As supper was being cooked by Phil, James announced that he had seen nine goslings running up the grey stony hills of the inner moraine. Finnur, Valli and I grabbed nets and joined him in pursuit. The goslings led us (me in gym shoes) over the stones, worn round and smooth by the glacier, to a lake beside which there were already about thirty more goslings with four or five adults. Pursuit over this rough going on foot was obviously fruitless. We divided up and I went off round the lake. Three goslings were left on the water, and one adult swimming low ahead of Valli. I climbed a steep soft hill with strange "quick-gravel" banks, and from there watched James crouching and waiting for the goslings to emerge. In due course they came, peeping, and almost ran up to him. But when he finally gave chase they got back into the lake. Nothing daunted, James went in after them up to his knees and caught one gosling—our fifty-third goose of the day.

"Before leaving the top of my hillock I saw about forty geese on a further lake, to the south. They had seen me and were swimming away. It is evident that there must be many flightless geese on these morainal lakes, but it will be impossible to ride after them, so they will be a dead loss to us.

"I came down the hill, past the largest and most wonderful

clump of yellow *Saxifraga hirculus*, and so to ring the little gosling and have an excellent beef stew, at our new and quite comfortable camp.

Saxifraga hirculus

"*Sat. 21 July.* It stopped raining about 8.0 a.m., and intermittent sun made the tent very hot. Now I sit in the sun after breakfast. Finnur has already found some exciting new flowers:

Habenaria viridis (*Coeloglossum viride*). Frog Orchid.
Epilobium sp. (probably *lactiflorum*), white willow-herb.
Botrychium lunaria. Maidenhair type fern. (This we have found before.)

He also brought some very fine *Veronica fruticans* and *Pyrola minor.*

"Yesterday he found a new *Carex*, as yet unidentified.

"To-day we go on to Arnarfellsbrekka, the rich vegetation at the foot of Arnarfell (the Eagles' Mountain). Higher on the hill behind Finnur hopes to find rarities, for it was evidently a nunatak in the Ice Age and has therefore been bare of ice for a very long time.

"*7.45 p.m.* We are back at our camp on the outer moraine in Múlaver, after a very pleasant, if less than usually anserine day.

"No sooner had we started, after I had filmed some flowers—the orchid and the eyrarros (*Chamaenerion latifolium*)—than the eagle came sweeping in from the marsh and settled on the moraine. From about 200 yards I tried to film him, but he flew and settled farther into the grey waste of stones. I stalked this time and got to within 100 yards. The bird was against the sky and I got a very short shot of him before he took off and flew on along the moraine.

"There were a few geese feeding on the marsh, but an attempt to drive them towards the moraine totally failed. They just went farther out into the marsh. We rode along the edge of the outer moraine with soft lush green bog on our right. A young dunlin, only just able to fly, ran up a mound. He had a short-tailed look—and a short bill too. This is the first baby dunlin we have seen. At some places the moraine mounds are 30 feet high, but as we proceeded they became lower. At one point there was a wide expanse of stony river bed. Apparently one year the Arnarfellskvísl ran through there and washed all the moraines away—outer and inner.

" Later we came to the shingle beds of this year's Arnarfells-kvísl, and to the stream itself, which was the swiftest water we have so far had to cross.

" The grey stones of the dry river beds are greatly enriched by patches, in places almost beds, of brilliant purplish pink—the eyrarros. The effect with a shimmer of heat-haze is marvellous on these great expanses of grey shingle, otherwise only broken by small patches of yellow-green moss.

" Arnarfell is a steep red mountain with green lower slopes, about 1,600 feet higher than the surrounding plateau. It lies in a cleft between two great tongues of glacier, with a half circle of lesser mountains at its back. As we drew near, it towered above us, and a wild gorge bordered with screes opened out to the south of it. The glacier tongue is held in by an ice-washed bastion with very steep cliffs which seemed a likely place for an Iceland falcon. But as we approached the main mountain Finnur spotted a bird of prey standing on a green ledge far, far up. We thought it was an Iceland falcon, perhaps even a this year's fledgling, but later, when we had dismounted and were looking at the flowers along the foot of the mountain, the bird took off, and soared out from the slope. It was our friend the eagle again. As we came to the bank my horse stepped on to a most innocent-looking patch of moss-covered shingle and went straight down with all four feet. I jumped off quick, and he turned so that I led him out, none the worse. Such a thing in the middle of a river would have been much less pleasant.

"The flowers on the lowest slope of the mountain, a few feet up from the flat gravel plain, were indeed striking. There was, for example, a great bed of purple-blue cranesbills (*Geranium sylvaticum*), with one freak plant among them—almost white with a tinge of lilac. Among them, to make the colour by contrast richer yet, were buttercups and *Potentilla verna*. All this was in great profusion and richness, and there was also a lush growth of *Archangelica*, although this had suffered largely from the passage of the first sheep which we could see ahead of us. It seems that they have a predilection for the plant and go from head to head eating off the great bulbous umbelliferous buds.

"We walked along the flat at the foot of the slope, finding upon it, and upon the rather steep bank which rises only a few feet above it, a number of new plants and a most luxuriant growth of many old ones. *Veronica fruticans*, the superb speedwell, was in evidence together with *V. alpina*. There was a new pink plant, very small and varying in intensity of colour, *Sedum villosum*; rich thyme and many saxifrages—*S. caespitosa* (*groenlandica*), *S. cernua*, *S. nivalis*, *S. stellaris*, and a new white one, very delicate and pretty, *S. hypnoides*. But king of all the saxifrages was the marvellous yellow *S. hirculus*. Hitherto we have seen it growing in ones and twos—at most four or five flowers—all over the brown parts of the tundra (the lumps and ridges in the tundra bogs). Sometimes among stones we have seen it, evidently thriving with up to a dozen flowers. But now suddenly we realised that the great yellow expanse which we had seen in the mirage a mile away, and taken for the very yellow moss which grows round springs, was in fact a field of yellow saxifrage growing in unimagined profusion, against a cushion of dark green moss. The star-shaped flowers of this lovely plant can be varied in shape, for sometimes the petals are full and round-tipped, at others pointed and more delicate. Here were all shapes and sizes—even a plant with near-white flowers which Finnur collected. For a flower which we already regarded as one of the most lovely up here, it was immensely exciting to see it in such a mass.

"Under the bank ran a mossy wet strip with occasional springs, and it was clear that a number of geese had been here recently. There were droppings and many moulted feathers. The geese had evidently been feeding on the yellow moss, which was pulled up in beakfuls. But only a part of it must have been eaten, the rest lying about untidily on the smooth moss sward.

"Among the *Archangelica* we found a sheltered bank for lunch. We chewed some flower stems of the great plant, but Phil does not like the taste and James found them too strong. We ate our corned beef and cheese, crisp-bread and biscuits, with dates for afters, and for part of the time it rained heavily.

"After lunch we planned to go up across the foot of a small and now detached glacier tongue to the vegetation patches on a slope beyond where Finnur hoped for rare plants. We walked along the foot of Arnarfell to the edge of the glacier. A common plant here was the sorrel-like *Oxyria digyna* with little round leaves. On the face of the mountain was the old mark of the lateral moraine—the "high-ice" mark, as it were. The glacier had long since retreated from here, but the stones had trickled down to make a protective layer under which was still ice—fossil ice almost. At one point there had been a subsidence of this ice, leaving an open ice cave and smooth glissades, with little landslides coming down it now and then. The cave was very impressive, the roof consisting of ice about eight feet thick, dripping continuously. Inside was a muddy pool, but the walls were of clear green ice and on one side we could see the stones bedded in the ice.

"Here there were recent mud slides, there were furrows where huge boulders as big as motor-cars had slithered down. The soil was soft and new—a landscape in the making.

Farther up we followed a small stream to its source under the lip of the glacier itself. There we found a young purple sandpiper, just able to fly, and filmed him.

"We climbed a little way on to the ice, which was uneven and pockmarked. In some places the very end of the glacier seemed to be pushing the mud and stones uphill on to the terminal moraines.

"At this point Phil discovered she had lost her watch—the little gold one she has had for seventeen years. She decided to retrace her course in hope of finding it. James went back with her and I went on to support Finnur and his botany. But when I had trudged through the soft moraines for a quarter of a mile I came up with Finnur, whose progress was barred by a roaring stream of turgid water. There was nothing to do but film its egress from the glacier and then turn back. Finnur had picked up a piece of obsidian—a lump of black glass about three inches long and one-and-a-half inches wide. It is used, he told me, in astronomical optics, and a piece weighing several tons was shipped to America last year. We walked back, I feeling somewhat awed by the elemental nature of these surroundings. I do not really like these lifeless moraines. Back on the green lower slope of Arnarfell we saw two wheatears. We had heard one before lunch. The two were evidently fledglings, and it seems probable that they were hatched here, so this is a doubtful addition to our list of breeding birds.

"We followed the wheatears up the slope a little, and from there looked out across the expanse of shingle, intermittently green between the wide beds of the glacial streams. There was a group of about twenty geese, mostly adults, feeding out there, perhaps the geese of which we had seen signs along the foot of the mountain.

"Back at the lunch place, Phil had not found her watch and James was asleep in the sun. We collected our bits and pieces and set off to ride back to our camp on the outer moraine of the main glacier tongue. On the way we started a female teal from a little open stream in the shingle. The crossing of the swift Arnarfellskvísl was negotiated without mishap, at the same point where the tracks of two lorries came to the river. These lorries, with about thirty men, had made an expedition up here last year, in late summer, in order to discover whether a tourist road could be opened in this part of the interior. They came up the east side of the Þjórsá, crossed it higher up and came back along this side. It seems unlikely that the country will be opened up in this way, and even if it were it would only be in late summer, when it would be unlikely to affect the geese.

" We rode along the crest of the uneven outer moraine all the way home counting pinkfoot nests—hatched and empty. From the start of the moraine to the Innri Múlakvísl—that is to say the part of the moraine which is in Arnarfellsver—we counted twenty-six nests, although I had a private list of seven which *could* at a pinch have been nests of the previous year. Nests with little down can be very deceptive, and the one near camp which hatched the day after we arrived, but had no down, now looks about three years old.

" After crossing the Innri Múlakvísl (not difficult where it comes through the moraine) we found nine more nests, plus three in the immediate vicinity of camp, so that up to here there have been thirty-eight nests. We shall count from here on as we go.

" Fifty yards short of camp we came upon a ptarmigan with small young. The young were about $4\frac{1}{2}$ inches long, but almost able to fly. We caught, eventually, five of them. The mother was very anxious and came fluttering round us, especially close to Finnur who had a baby in his hand. She ran about with open wings only three or four feet from him.

" We tagged the five young birds and then came into camp, and a supper of stewed steak and puff-balls. It was only about 8.0 so we got to bed early. After supper Finnur went botanising and found two new plants, both very tiny : *Ranunculus pygmaeus* already over—a minute buttercup—and the other perhaps *Koenigia islandica*, an even more minute group of white flowers nestling in three tiny leaves.

"During the night some geese came across the marsh near camp. At 5.30 I looked out, hearing continuous scolding from a whimbrel. I thought maybe it was the eagle, but I could see no eagle, only a crowd of fifty geese. The count was exactly fifty. There were about sixteen adults, the rest goslings. Two goslings were unattached but seemed to be getting along quite well.

"I saw an admirable family row in which goslings of both sides joined in. There was much neck lowering and false preening in the adults, but no evident victor and vanquished as there usually is in winter. Both sides stood their ground and passion gradually became spent.

"*Sun. 22 July*. It snowed, or rather sleeted early this morning. It's very cold. We plan to return to our base camp at Bólstaður by way of Nauthagi (pronounced Noitayi) where there is a specially large goose-fold. We must try to get some geese today.

"Our day began with a delightful ride along the moraine, counting nests. The final total in Múlaver was thirty-three empty nests. A small number may have been of previous seasons, but not many.

"The nest site of the pinkfoot is interesting. It is usually at the highest available point. This is particularly true in the marshes and tundra, rather less so on the mounds of the moraines. Here the gander's look-out post is at the highest point and the nest must be within about fifteen feet of it. There is evidently some important survival value in the two birds being close together, probably because only as a pair can they repel a predator—fox, falcon, gull, eagle, snowy owl.

"It is interesting that we have seen all these in action,

except the owl. I do not think the arctic skua is a first-hand predator except on unattended eggs.

"A small lake just inside the outer moraine contained a pair of swans. They seemed rather tame. Finnur dismounted to photograph them against the background of the glacier at a range of thirty or forty yards, in bright sun. They looked splendid. One bird flew off, but the other remained and it soon became evident that it had moulted and was flightless. We surrounded the lake, but the bird had the sense to remain on the water—which was very deep in parts. So having ineffectually lobbed stones behind it to persuade it to go ashore, and having photographed it, we accepted defeat and rode on.

"At one point on the moraine we came upon a bank of gentians. This was a small brilliant blue flower, *Gentiana nivalis.* It was a cold blue, contrasting with the warm blue of *Veronica fruticans* growing all round and among it. The yellow in the mixture was provided by *Hieracium* sp.—the hawkweed, now out in profusion on some parts of the moraine. At various points we had seen signs of the truck expedition of last summer—tracks and small cairns where they had camped for the night. Two such cairns together had been at Arnarfell. Now we found one with a bottle stuck into it. The bottle had a message inside. There was a poem, which Finnur declared was untranslatable, and there was record of the date (19 Sep. 1950) on which the camp had been made there.

"In due course we left the perimeter of the glacier's fan and, crossing the Fremri Múlakvísl into Illaver, set out across a stretch of shingle, sparsely covered with vegetation. Ahead was a low wave with a prominent goose-fold on it. We skirted this at first in order to surprise any geese beyond.

"We sighted one lot, far out, and galloped off after them, but they could go very fast on this kind of terrain. In some curious way they disappeared, but I saw some more running away to the right. The galloping cavalcade wheeled towards them, but once more they disappeared. This time, however, some of the goslings had crouched and we caught five of them—one with a lame left leg. We ringed it on the right leg, which is our convention for this year anyway.

"Then we went back to look at the goose-fold (Pl. 7*b*, p. 80). It was the best preserved of any we had seen, the walls still standing, and supported by vegetation growing in the sand which has silted up round it, inside and out. This fold is evidently contemporary with the first one we saw, near the summit of Nautalda, and I think, a good deal later than the much smaller and more ruinous ones we have found on the tops of so many hills.

"But this one had two new features. First it was curved, almost like a decoy pipe, and secondly it was only about fifty yards from the edge of the flat shingle beds on the least promising side. Thus it is evident that the geese were driven over the hill from the other side and swept round into the fold, which led uphill almost back in the direction from which they had come.

"The dimensions of this fold were about the same as those of the Nautalda one: 12 m. long and 2–2½ wide. At the blind end the wall was about 4½ ft. high. It seems possible that the wall was originally higher at the blind end than at the other, but this may be simply due to the drifting sands which have supported the wall at that end. There was a hatched empty nest against the wall. I am now absolutely satisfied that these folds cannot have been used without some kind of wings or leaders to funnel the geese into the trap. Had these wings been nets it is unlikely that a great stone structure would have been necessary. Why not a cage of net as well? Thus we must suppose that the wings were made of something which, although good enough for wings, was not good enough to hold a bulk of geese in the cage at the conclusion of the drive. For material for these wings we must look to the most easily available and cheapest. Horse-hair ropes, no doubt, were available, but probably fairly valuable, and a rope by itself, although possibly effective far out on the wings, could not have been enough to steer the geese into the walled enclosure.

" The easiest thing to get on the spot would be the roots and stems of *Salix glauca* and *Salix lanata*. These form a sort of tangle, with long roots which could be tied together and would form a network sufficiently impervious to geese for the wings of the trap but not for the cage. I believe the wings of these traps to have been made of this *Salix* scrub, anchored with stones (but see page 146).

" The insides of the folds might well repay excavation. So too might a small square of stones which we found on the shingle flat below and which had evidently once been a house.

" Twenty minutes later we had sighted another bunch of geese and we galloped down after them across a much richer meadow. The geese got to the Miklakvísl and we abandoned them, returning to the richest part of the meadow, where a small notice on a post proclaimed that we were at Nauthagi. Under the word ' Nauthagi ' was the date 1928 and the letters O.B., standing for Ólafur Bergsson, who put up the notice (celebrated by a big party with spirits and cakes) on the occasion of his fiftieth visit. He was farmer at Skríðufell just opposite Ásólfsstaðir. He was *fjäll kongur* (' mountain-king') that is, in complete control of all sheep-collecting operations, and is now buried at his farm, with his horse. Nauthagi means ' the Bull Meadow,' and Nautalda means ' the Bull Wave.' It seems that a bull once spent the winter here by itself, feeding on the lush grass. We soon found out why the grass was so lush here. There were springs, and they were hot springs (see sketch-map, p. 161). In some of the creeks or rivulets, banked with mosses and rich vegetation, there were large numbers of sticklebacks. In one stream, where the water ran down a six-inch wide channel, there were a lot of dead sticklebacks which had evidently cooked themselves.

" For the last two hours the wind blowing off the glacier

had been very strong and very cold. It was mid-wintery weather, after the snow of the early morning (which had left the Tungnafellsjökull and its perimeter of mountains all white). So we dabbled our hands in the warm water. We found one spring in which we could only just bear the temperature. It was most soothing.

"But Finnur was having the most exciting time, for he had found almost a dozen new species of plants clustered in this little oasis of warmth. There were the dark red rather dried-up looking flowers of *Comarum palustre*; the three-lobed leaves of bog-bean (*Menyanthes trifoliata*); there was yellow rattle (*Rhinanthus minor*); and a tiny delicate white *Stellaria crassifolia*; a new willow-herb (*Epilobium palustre*), to me very much like *alsinifolium*; there was the maidenhair-like fern *Botrychium lunaria*; and most exciting of all, its very rare relation *Ophioglossum vulgatum*, a smooth tongue-like leaf with a green flower still in bud, not more than three inches high (snake's tongue), unexciting to look at, perhaps, but so rare, Finnur told us, that its localities in Iceland are each mentioned by name in the *Flora*. This is a new locality for it. There was also a pretty moss holding silver drops of water on it, pale grey-green and unusual.

"While Finnur was botanising, Valli had somewhere found a gosling, which was duly ringed and released. I collected some algae from the hot springs for Edward Hindle. We did not have a thermometer with us, and he had indicated that the exact temperature was important. But there seemed to be a fairly wide latitude in the requirements of this particular alga, between water which was only just bearable to the immersed hand, down to water which just felt warm—i.e. from 110° F. down to about 75° F. James collected a spider, which was probably the same as we have found already.

"In the middle of the cluster of springs (some incidentally cold) was a mound with a goose nest on it, and *Sedum roseum* growing on it.

"This was evidently a traditional nest of great antiquity, and it is exciting to think of the generations of geese, perhaps reaching back to the days of the goose-folds, seven centuries or more ago, which have been hatched at that precise spot. We found the flank feather of a drake teal among the hot springs, and then we rode on, crossing the Miklakvísl and coming to the cold springs at the foot of Nautalda, where we had lunched before. Here we lunched again, in a cold wind with a huge dark cloud hanging above us. This cloud, in the lee of the glacier, was quite stationary, a front with blue sky over the ice and cloudy greyness perpetually over us, so it seemed. Two new plants here, *Juncus arcticus*, a very ordinary looking rush, and *Selaginella selaginoides*, the familiar lycopod, just now beginning to appear.

"I put on more clothes from my rucksack and felt warmer as we rode on round the foot of the hill on the N.W. side. We passed a single goose walking out on to the marsh. Perhaps because it was alone it walked out in quite a leisurely fashion. But the stream between us and it was reputedly too soft to follow. At the south end of the hill we came upon about forty geese and a long hunt ensued. The geese went out across a wide shingle stretch beyond the hill. Unfortunately a soft patch of marsh held us up, but Valli and Phil got through this. Had the shingle beyond been hard we might have made a big catch, but it was soft enough to prevent the ponies from going really fast. James and I tried to go round the marsh, which took us far off our course. Finnur came on behind with the pack ponies.

"When we got out on to the shingle we found many soft places which looked unbelievably innocent. James got into one of these, and his pony went in up to the hocks. He just got it out without having to dismount. I went off away to the left in pursuit of two goslings, and eventually Phil came too, and we got them both.

"We gathered together on this open tract of gravel for the

ringing operation. The wind was now gale force and the battle of the clouds was at its height. An enormous sharp-edged cumulus cloud gave space to the sun, and we were at once warmer. We had caught two adult geese and five goslings, but two of them were almost fully fledged. These must have been at least six weeks old and were taken for adults during catching.

" As we rode on towards the Blautakvísl the weather once more became a feature of our day. The wind came in gusts and whirls which brought clouds of dust, sweeping up in ominous yellow smoke wreaths. We got caught in it for a moment and our horses began to trot, whipped into it by the cutting grit. And then it had passed and we watched the yellow cloud blowing away. The wind was still chill, but the day had suddenly smiled on us. We rode across Blautakvísl and on to Ptarmigan Lake, but no geese. Over the ridge beside an attractive lake, which we have called Philsvatn, James cried ' tally-ho ' and a new chase was on, rather a long one, as the geese were about 500 yards away at the start. Eventually, however, Phil and Valli got amongst them on a low stony ridge (on which was yet another small early goose-fold) and the birds crouched all around.

" This was very typical of our hunts and emphasised the highly sporting character of our ringing activities. A sharp gallop over awkward ground, after which some of the adults and most of the young crouch. But there is a marked distinction between the behaviour of the two, for whereas the adults usually remain crouched during a stealthy approach from the dismounting place ten yards away, and can be picked up by hand, the goslings always start running again at about three or four yards. The goslings can be caught after an all-out zigzag run of about 100 yards, especially if they can be turned to run downhill, when human legs have the advantage. James's nets, large mesh net stretched on soft wire at the end of one of the aluminium uprights of one of Eric Hosking's hides (those of the other support our wireless aerial at the tent end) . . . these nets greatly facilitate capture at the last moment, and shorten the sprint by a most welcome amount. If the adults start to run again it is almost useless to pursue on foot, again unless they are going downhill. On this particular occasion, having twice failed, on dismounting, to pick up one adult, I did finally over-run it downhill and persuade it to crouch until captured. We forgathered with some of the catch on the summit of the ridge and then sighted another young one trying to creep away. Then two, and when Valli and I reached the spot there were three. Finnur came to the rescue and we caught all three. We had begun the ringing when Finnur suddenly spotted another adult, about 100 yards away, crouching by a big rock. It had shifted its position, which movement drew his eye to it. Again the hunt was on. Valli leaped to horse. The bird broke and ran for it, and Valli had a long hunt, ultimately driving it to James, who got it with a tennis shot. Thus at the end of a most sportive chase we had fifteen geese (four adults). After the hunt we saw two goslings making off in the opposite direction to that in which the ringed ones had been released. Valli went off after them, but found that the bird he caught was in fact one just ringed. However, the pursuit led Phil to a sandy flat on which she found a newly hatched ringed plover with an injury-feigning mother.

" We made a detour to approach the hill lake above Pintail Marsh and then found that a small bunch of geese were on the far side, where we might have got them had we gone directly to it.

" Our next geese appeared close in front of us at the very softest part of the middle of Deserted Swan Marsh. This was very bad luck, because the geese were so close at the outset that many were crouching around, and two even *in* the muddy stream which drains the marsh. Valli and I went across and on up the hill over into the little valley which James calls

Failure Creek, the valley next to Bólstaður and our camp. Here I caught an adult and Phil later had a great chase after a gosling on a lake, which swam from one side to the other. This was a most important gosling because it was tagged C. 506—that is to say, it was one of the first two broods to be tagged and was from nest 4 or 5 (I did not write down the two separately). The most notable feature of this gosling is that its age was known exactly (twenty-five days), and that its size was strikingly small. It was only just unnecessary to flatten the ring. By this measurement of size it seems likely that my estimate of five to six days old for the young we caught in Oddkelsver on 2 July (which were a very average size when recaptured on 17 July) was too low. They may have originally been ten days old. If so, it must take the average hatching date back from 26 June to 22, perhaps 20, which in turn means complete clutches by 24 May and first eggs 12 May.

"James had a fruitless hunt on foot right up the marsh, which left the pack ponies unattended, much to Valli's alarm and despondency, because the two got separated, and he fears a disaster with the ponies getting frightened and bolting, scattering the contents of the packs all around. James's excursion, however, disclosed a scaup with four small ducklings. This might be the bird from the nest we found in Chipping Swan Marsh, but is most probably a new one.

"We returned to find everything all right at our Base Camp, and there were thirty-five geese in the hollow at the mouth of the iron stream, 100 yards from our mess tent. They went off down stream in the Þjórsá. Later, in the low evening sunlight, and amazing clarity of atmosphere, we watched about thirty geese on the sand at the mouth of the Blautakvísl, and more away across the Þjórsá sands at the edge of Þúfuver and Biskupsþúfa (Thoovoo-vair and Bisküpsthoova).

"We made contact of a sort with Gufunes, but could not explain that we had been away for two nights. He could not read us, but broadcast a curious and evidently faulty message, the sense of which was, however, quite plain.

> ' Reykjavík No. 104.7982. 12 words.
> Handed in : *20th July 16.30.*
> Addressed to : *Hofsjökull Expedition Sunderland via T F W*
> Message : *Still delayed will advise when we hear, Greenway.*'

Clearly ' Sunderland ' should have been the first word of the message.

" I forgot to mention that during the day, on a shingle-bank, we saw a very beautiful distraction-display by a ringed plover with small young."

Injury-feigning Ringed Plover

CHAPTER XI

The Day of Frustration

ON 25 JULY we rested the horses for a day, brought our diaries up to date, and washed—even shaving came into the day's programme! We discussed plans and results, and came to the general conclusion that we were doing something wrong. Although we had ringed altogether no less than 268 geese and goslings, we felt we were not making the best of our opportunities, not catching enough of a population that was proving to be surprisingly large—working, in fact, in an exhausting and wasteful way. Such was the situation when the expedition decided to make a crossing of the river Þjórsá to taste the goose-density on the other side, and to find a more efficient way of driving and catching the pinkfeet of the Þjórsárver.

It had been a very cold sunset and it was an unpleasantly cold night. James woke several times with cold and, in wriggling about to dodge the draught, tore the inner lining of his ancient sleeping-bag. He came into the mess-tent for breakfast on 24 July looking like a snowstorm. During the night an arctic fox barked several times in Oddkelsver, a triple coughing bark. The morning hoar-frost made the glaucous willows a cold green, like crystallised angelica. But as soon as the sun had shaken off the skyline of the ice-cap, it was bright, and soon it began to be warm. A swan flew past as Peter emerged from his tent, and over in Oddkelsver he saw three groups of geese and a few sheep.

We were now much attached to our base camp in this glorious place; the only disadvantage of our particular part of the oasis was the fairly high density of animals in the drinking water: no doubt they were very nourishing and full of vitamins. When the expedition got back to England, J. P. Harding of the Natural History Museum identified a dozen different sorts, of which by far the commonest was a Copepod called *Diaptomus castor*.

The main tent, the big white, Scottish-made "Iceland" tent, was extremely well organised (by Phil) and quite comfortable. The floor, which was moss and grass—to begin with—was now somewhat the worse for wear, and dusty; but otherwise the accommodation was very good. Just inside the door on the right was a group of ration-boxes on their sides, their pigeon-holes filled with food-tins: this was the larder. Next came another box with the two Primuses sitting on it. In the middle of the tent was a wooden box full of biscuits with a cardboard table top attached to it, the corners carefully rounded off—all this the work of James. The dining-room table was a source of great pride and gratification to all. The expedition sometimes sat down to meals with a tablecloth, and always with a vase (empty tin) of flowers in the middle of the table—sometimes thrift, sometimes thyme, very often the pinkish-mauve, orchid-like *Viscaria alpina*. Ranged round the walls of the tent were kitbags and more ration-boxes, full and empty (or at least empty of food, and filled with films, books and things). There was a string along the wall of the tent on which were hung washing-up cloths and socks. On the far tent-pole from the door hung Finnur's gun (scarcely used), and behind the pole he stowed his air-mattress, as he slept in the mess-tent. We sat on ration-boxes, using various forms of padding. James had thoughtfully brought two air-cushions, one of which was lent to Phil. Peter brought in his sleeping bags every morning, rolled up as a cushion. The last side of the tent was Finnur's department (collecting gear, plant presses); it contained also the tool-box, and the wooden box to which was attached the generator of the radio, and beyond that was the transmitter-receiver itself, next to the door, so that we could lead in the aerial and the earth.

At breakfast Valli interrupted a general discussion of the relative merits of cameras to report (Finnur rapidly translating) great quantities of geese south of the camp (which he had seen when he went to get the horses), including about sixty in the mouth of the iron stream quite close to the camp. We discussed setting a net here, when we had come back from the other side of the river.

Although not more than twenty miles from its main source, the River Þjórsá as it flowed across the great plateau near the camp was in places quite a mile wide, ramifying intricately through sands and alluvium which it had brought down in past ages. Just by the camp, however, it narrowed to a quarter of a mile, to flow off the plateau down minor rapids between two headlands. The farmers' crossing was just above these rapids, and it was this that Valli had successfully tried on horseback the day before. It was now the time for the entire party to explore the mysteries of the left bank.

We all crossed at about eleven-thirty, on our horses, wearing outer mackintosh trousers fastened with strings to the tops of our Wellingtons. The crossing was from camp to sandbank (up to the horses' knees), from sandbank to sandbank (bellies), from sandbank to stony island (bellies) and from stony island to the headland Sóleyjarhöfði (hocks, and in one place bellies). The last part of the crossing was difficult, with large round boulders on the floor of the river. But all the ponies behaved wonderfully well, and James only stumbled once. So we were all over the famous crossing, dry and ready for anything; and after a certain amount of debagging among the buttercups of Buttercup Headland, we set off to explore the unexplored. We rode up the green hill and looked over the valley beyond.

Down on our right a small party of geese was moving away. With the glasses Peter could see a much bigger bunch half hidden under the hill; these had not yet begun to move. The expedition withdrew, and trotted along the blind side of a ridge so as to come out opposite them. When we came over we found a large crowd of geese, fully fifty, and galloped down into the marsh. Phil and Valli were all among the young, but a big contingent went up the steep slope beyond, and they roared after them. It looked as though it should be a good do, but somehow, surprisingly, it was rather a failure. At the end the catch was only nine goslings and three adults, but we got five more rather large goslings half a mile on down the valley, which were obviously a product of this hunt.

One of the adults, a gander, had a broken tarsus which had completely mended. This was the right leg, and although we could easily have put a ring on above the swollen joint, we thought that anyone recovering the bird later would be bound to attribute the injury to the ring, so we ringed the left leg instead.

We rode along the bank of a tributary of the Þjórsá known as the Þúfuverskvísl, with a high ridge on our right, and presently we saw a crowd of thirty or forty geese going up it. It was a forlorn hope really, but Valli went crashing off. Already this same ridge, farther back, had tired the horses at the first hunt, and this second climb finished them and yielded only fifteen goslings. But it gave us an addition to our technique. A gosling crouched far ahead of Peter; he approached it in a wide curve, leaned down with his net, scooped it off the ground, brought it up to the saddle and transferred it to his sack, all without dismounting. The horse didn't mind this at all, and behaved with exemplary *sang froid.*

The Þúfuverskvísl was a clear river, a snow-stream, not a glacier-stream; it made the water of the extreme left of the Þjórsá also clear for quite some distance below its entry, as we found on our crossing. There were many snow-buntings about, some with flying broods, and meadow-pipits; on dry patches of vegetation, whimbrels, and golden plover and dunlins. Over a marsh flew a pair of arctic terns. Presently we came round a headland into sight of the main marsh of the Þúfuver (which means the Meadow of the Mounds). At once

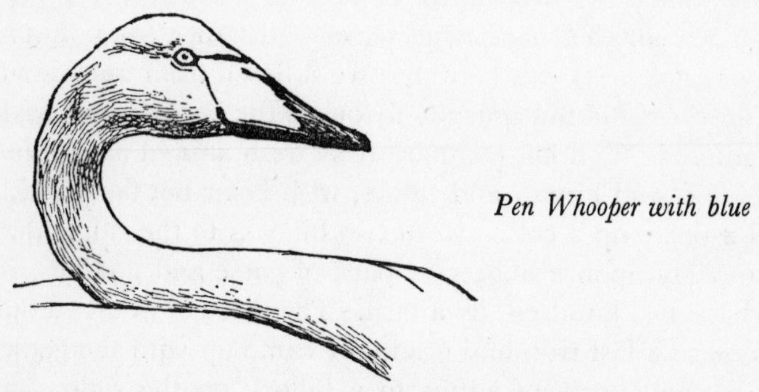

Pen Whooper with blue eyes

we were faced by a deep creek with tangled banks, upon which was much vegetation. We found some plants we had not seen before, and James saw a bumble-bee here. It was certainly an area of eminently goose-worthy tundra bog, and following the creek, we counted thirteen empty hatched nests of pinkfeet on its dry banks in a few minutes. All of a sudden James's horse shied and deposited him neatly on the ground.

The horse had shied at a brood of whooper swans under the bank—cob, pen and three cygnets, two or three weeks hatched. The cob was still able to fly and went off, returning after a few minutes; the pen, however, had already moulted, and was bravely ready to protect her young. The creek was not very easy to cross, except for Peter in long rubber boots, and the swan kept in the stream although it was only a few feet wide. Eventually, after a violent wet chase, Valli caught it, while James and Phil caught the three cygnets. A remarkable feature of the pen was that the irises of her eyes were a pale grey-blue, and marbled—this was quite different from the normal dark brown eyes of this species, exemplified by Daisy, the adult whooper at the New Grounds in Gloucestershire.

We all photographed the swans in colour and black and white, tagged them and then let them go, and had an agreeable (if fly-blown) sunny lunch under the bank near the ruins of an old shelter hut. The horses had a good grazing place.

After lunch we continued along the cairned track and encountered another pack of geese, some distance away by the shores of a lake. It was here that we suffered from indecision. Valli, for once, did not spur madly on, as the horses were tired. Phil cantered off on her comparatively fresh animal after some of the geese, and Finnur and James, with Peter not far behind, chased a party up a col between two hillocks to the ridge, and came quickly upon a huge new pack of geese and goslings, in all perhaps two hundred, by a tarn. The three of us urged our ponies on to a fast trot, and gradually came up with the geese, losing a small party of adults to a hillock on the right, but edging the vast majority up a steep hill to the left, along which the ponies, fortunately, could trot. Over this hill we confidently expected to see Valli and Phil, for they had last been seen going in that direction.

Presently, over the hill, we found ourselves the agents of a classic round-up. Our three ponies stood on three sides and for a moment held calmly packed and quiet, immobile, bunched solid, at least a hundred and fifty geese, mostly goslings.

Then an adult ran downhill, and it was as if the key log of a dam had slipped, for the situation at once collapsed, and the goose pack scattered in every direction, leaving us to gather what we could. James, probably wrongly, charged off downhill to get a gosling at the edge of the marsh, where he got off his horse. Peter and Finnur stayed up the hill. Valli came up hastily from half a mile away in response to urgent signals. Phil was nowhere to be seen. We fought to glean what we could from the lost harvest. James returned uphill to field another gosling, chased it downhill with his net, and turned his ankle painfully. It was Valli who caught the gosling. By the time Phil rode back, having pursued and caught three geese of her own, we were all seething with frustration.

There were no recriminations, for was it not in the drill that Valli and Phil should press on at best speed? The separation of our forces was a mistake of our own agreed policy. But Peter went so far as to say that never in the whole of his goosing career had he lost such a mighty opportunity.

We were exhausted and disappointed. The pack-horses were out of sight, Phil had had to catch one of her goslings twice when it escaped from her bag, and during the ringing operations we all fumbled so much that two more goslings escaped and had to be caught again, and then an adult escaped and was finally recovered by Valli about three hundred yards away.

But how could we have exploited the situation without nets? A net in the right place, on what we now called Frustration Hill, would have landed us with at least a hundred geese and an hour's ringing—perhaps two hundred. If all five riders had been together, could we have surrounded the pack and let them out a few at a time to be caught individually? Could we have rushed in among the geese, brandishing our hand nets, and kept them crouched? Could we have intimidated them by shouting? What the hell could we have done? Answer: at least better than five adults and ten goslings, which is all we got.

As the horses were tired we started back for the Þjórsá, and on the next hill south immediately fell in with a pack of goslings, of which, for once, we caught nearly all we saw—

eight—bringing the day's total to fifty-five, a record for a day's work, but somehow a very disappointing record. But we got these goslings at some cost, for as a result of this hunt we lost one horseman, at least temporarily.

When James had twisted his ankle on Frustration Hill, Peter had warned him to be careful of it. This warning he forgot in a headlong chase after a gosling. Twice it crouched and twice it beat his hand net, and on its third run James thought he had it, when it somersaulted down a bank of large loose stones. Instead he came over on his already weakened ankle, turning it over sole inwards and coming down on it with all his sixteen stone from a four-foot jump. He immediately dropped his net and sack and staggered, unable to stop, another twenty or thirty yards, and ended up below the once more crouched gosling, in a trauma, so that he could only wave to Valli and point wordlessly to the gosling, which Valli easily caught.

Somebody brought James his horse, but he had to get off it at the top of the hill and lie down for a bit, as the external world was beginning to withdraw. It came back as the others were rounding up the last goslings and ringing them, and afterwards he felt better and improved in health and spirits as we went home; he kept his gumboot on as a tight dressing, and his by then throbbing ankle was much cooled, in a very pleasant way, by the return crossing of the Þjórsá, which had risen two or three inches. We crossed without mishap in the evening sunshine.

James's foot was pretty blue and swollen when the boot came off, and chasing geese on foot was out for him for the rest of the trip; and of this we only had about a week left before we had to start back. With the total catch at 323 Peter doubted if the total would reach five hundred, which was the figure we had set ourselves as "complete success."

Back in camp James's (medicinal) ankle-brandy somehow became tots all round, and we all settled down to cheerful talk and nonsense, in spite of the frustrations of the day. The complete and unbroken harmony which had reigned over the whole party for all those weeks in the oasis was almost unprecedented.

Radio conditions were hopeless in the evening, which was once more very cold, with a marvellous sunset lighting the snow peaks of Tungnafellsjökull with luminous pink. There was a chill north wind which blew all night.

CHAPTER XII

The Day of Success

NEXT DAY, 25 July, Peter was woken at 3.15 a.m. by the distant drone of aero-engines. Could this be the expected Sunderland to drop mail and films? He emerged to find the most brilliant red dawn, and a distant speck of an aircraft which looked like a Catalina crossing from Reykjavík to Seyðisfjörður—though why at 3 a.m. seemed obscure.

At 8.0 it was blowing hard, still from the north, and cloudy and cold. We were going over to Oddkelsver to try some catching in our rabbit-nets, already set on stakes at the top of the grey hill there—all except James, who was confined to camp with his ankle. We set off about 12.30, crossing Blautakvísl, and, dividing up immediately, Finnur and Peter forked left across the marsh, while Phil and Valli rode up the Þjórsá bank. We had agreed to emerge upon the marsh (now known as Falcon Marsh) at 14.10.

Finnur and Peter found a party of geese at the exact spot where we had previously made our best hunt-catch. They moved on to the hill ahead. It seemed they might be driven into the nets, so just before Foxwarren the party subdivided,

Finnur with the pack-pony going up over the ridge, while Peter rode round the foot of the hill. Near Foxwarren these geese, and many more, came into view, and began heading for the north crest of Oddkelsalda; but they slipped out to the left and crossed the Miklakvísl. At the time Peter thought Finnur was going too fast, and shouted and waved frantically,

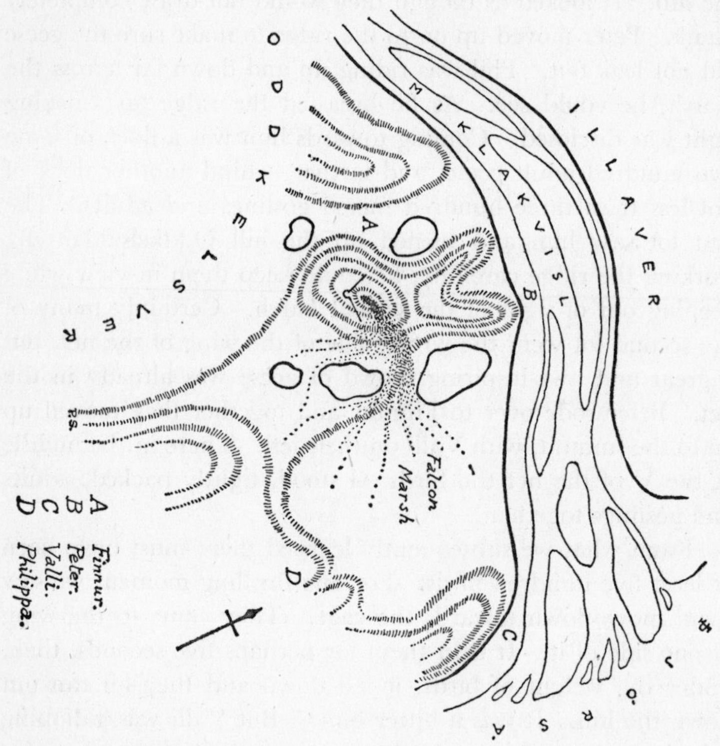

and successfully, to hold him back. But when the last of the goose families—two hundred strong in all—had crossed the stream into Illaver, he rode over and joined Finnur, feeling already slightly despondent and frustrated. All our trust would now have to be placed in the marsh on the other side of the hill, where we could hear at least one goose calling.

Peter dismounted when he came to the point at Miklakvísl (B) and peeped over. Not a goose was to be seen on the green marsh. When there were still two minutes to go he saw Valli ride out from his corner (C), so he mounted and emerged himself. At first he could see nothing. Then he saw three or four adults and a few young making their way up to the top of the hill. It looked as though they would not draw completely blank. Peter moved up on to the ridge to make sure the geese did not leak out. Phil was riding up and down far across the marsh, he could see. As he breasted the ridge an amazing sight was disclosed. Coming towards him was a flock of some two hundred adult geese, and farther behind another flock of not less than three hundred mixed goslings and adults. The first lot saw him and turned up the hill Oddkelsalda. By working the ridge carefully, he could keep them in view while keeping out of sight of the second batch. Certainly many of the second lot went the wrong side of the wing of the net, but a great and awe-inspiring crowd of geese was already in the net. Peter rode over to Finnur, and together they moved up on to the summit, with Valli on their left. There in the middle of the V of the net the birds all stood, tightly packed, adults and goslings together!

From what we subsequently learned there must have been at least five hundred birds. For one thrilling moment we saw them move down towards the cage. They came to the wing at one side of it. It held them for perhaps five seconds, then, under the weight of birds, it fell down and they all ran out down the hill. It was a bitter blow. But Valli was galloping round them, and soon many were on their way up again. Peter had put up the net again, but in a few minutes the geese were against it on the wrong side. Again in a matter of seconds it was down again and the stream of geese had run through on to the top of the hill; now they were back on the right side of the net but heading for the Miklakvísl.

Finnur and Valli came in and cut off the stream before

many had gone, and once more a phalanx of geese was standing on top of the hill. Now the four of us were on all four sides of the geese, and a state of near-equilibrium had been reached. This was the critical moment. Could we keep them there long enough to repair and strengthen the net? How long would they be ready to stand in a bunch on the crest of the hill without making a determined effort to break out? Already some individuals were making minor sallies to test the siege. But the goose crowd seemed to offer some kind of refuge, for as soon as the breakaway geese were headed they ran back into the crowd and were, it seemed, relieved to be in the thick of the flock again. A few geese had become tangled on the wrong side of the net when they went back over it. These Phil and Peter now extricated, ringed and released (five or six goslings and two adults). That got them out of the way. Then Peter went down to the end of the wings to get stakes, not now needed out there, to strengthen the cage and the wings near it. While this was going on, Valli and Finnur stood behind the geese, about ten yards from them. Finnur's horse and the pack-horse came down one side of the geese, almost spoiling everything, but finally, instead, acting as additional stops.

At one stage Phil said they must take a photo of it. Peter agreed as long as Finnur didn't see, for poor Finnur, it seemed, was in an agony of mind about the situation and kept urging haste, saying that he did not think they could keep the geese in much longer! Peter kept calling to Finnur not to worry but just to keep them in—which he most skilfully did.

It transpired later that Finnur had clandestinely taken an excellent series of photos, hoping that Peter would not see him doing so and think that he was not paying attention to the main task (Pl. 12*a*, p. 177).

At last all was ready. The cage was as strong as we could make it. Phil drew back, keeping to the same side so as to hold the geese up if they began to break through. Peter moved round a little, and the whole flock began to move down the slope almost without knowing it was moving. It was at this stage that, for the second time, Peter remembered to look for blue rings (birds ringed by himself and Phil in Scotland or perhaps on the Wash). The first time he had seen none, but now, right in front, he could see a bright blue ring. He shouted to Phil, who was equally thrilled when she saw it.

The geese went into the cage, though it would scarcely hold them all. Peter was for bringing round one of the wings to enclose them from behind so as to have a much larger cage, but Finnur thought they might get them all into the cage, and we found, when they were all in, that there was just room for them. The cage was five yards by about three, more or less oval.

Now the mystery of the goose-folds was solved. No wings had been necessary, no nets, nothing but the stone pen. A few more riders would have been necessary, but ten would be ample; the birds would be rounded up on the top of the hill, and then edged gently towards the fold. That was evidently the whole story, and it was very fascinating to have tested it in this way. So much for the elaborate theories about horse-hair ropes and networks of dwarf willow! With our geese safely in the cage, Valli finally pulled up one wing of the net and brought it across to use as a door. With the cage so full we couldn't get at the door we had originally provided.

Now the worst trouble was that if the party approached the cage the geese would crowd to the opposite side, climbing on each other's backs; there were at this time about three hundred geese and goslings in the cage. Another trouble was that the top line of the net began to slip down the stakes as the net was bulged out by the weight. In this way, during the next hour or so, about thirty geese escaped in ones and twos. Some got out at the joint of the new door; one or two through holes in the net. Valli broke out a badly tangled bird, leaving a gaping hole in the net. These were all the difficulties, but by and large matters were under control, and we soon fell into a quite satisfactory drill. Phil got into the cage and caught the birds, adults one at a time, goslings two at a time, bringing them to Peter to be ringed. Finnur was on the opposite side writing down, and Valli was free to move about, make minor repairs, disentangle birds about to hang themselves and so on, while Peter ringed on. In due course we came to the blue-ringed bird which turned out to be No. 129984.

In this account it has been said that three hundred geese went into the cage, but at the time the party had no idea what the number was. Peter had 130 rings with him. Whenever a bird escaped he said to Finnur, who was always much concerned about it, "Never mind—we have far more than we have rings for." He was not even sure of that, but thought so, and eventually it became evident that this was the case. When he had no more than a handful of rings left on the string there was still a sufficient number of geese in the cage to make it worth while for Valli to go back to the camp for more rings. While he was away the geese in the cage were rested. Most of the goslings sat down and went to sleep quite happily. Eventually Valli came riding back. He had Peter's horse with him, which had wandered away a bit. He had been away for less than an hour. We got to work again and ringed the rest of the geese in the cage.

Meanwhile, in camp, James was finding his ankle standable but not walkable on, as expected, and was writing up his diary, trying to make some swan rings out of goose rings (the expedition had forgotten to bring any of swan size), screwing the radio dynamo on to a new stand, and washing. He had his first hot water bath for a month by instalments, washed some clothes, trimmed his beard, played a game of patience and cooked a good lunch. When Valli came cantering up for what James quickly guessed were more rings, the situation became mysterious. It surely meant either splendid forgetfulness or a splendid catch: and the mystery deepened when

James looked at the catching-pen, three miles away on the hill, through his glass, and saw nobody. This was, as it turned out, because Peter, Phil and Finnur had sat down in a withdrawn spot. But an hour after Valli had left with a string of rings James saw the horses by the pen and human figures moving busily about. They were still there after a further hour and a half. " Are they just taking up the nets ? " he wrote in his diary. " Or have they caught half the geese in the Þjórsárver ? If the latter, why does this bloody ankle prevent me from being in on it ! "

When Valli returned to the goose-net, what Peter had thought to be sixty, perhaps more, turned out to be 118, and included another blue-ringed bird. When we looked these up later we found that one had been marked in October in south-east Scotland, and the other in December on the Wash. Thus the total number ringed was 247 (ninety-four adults), plus six local recaptures (two adults), plus two recaptures of British ringed birds. When the last geese had been released the party went down to the little pool to the west of the hill and had lunch. It was about 6.0 p.m.

Afterwards we went up and re-set the net with a larger cage of improved design.

One very curious thing had been happening. On the middle lake of the marsh from which we had drawn the geese there had been a bunch of geese all through the ringing operations, although the workers were in full view and only about four hundred yards away. Many of the released birds must have gone down there, because the number steadily increased. They sat on the water, mostly, but after a while they began to feed quite unconcernedly on the far bank. This behaviour was in marked contrast to anything which we had seen before. After lunch we saw a possible cause. Sitting on a mound in the marsh beyond was a huge, pale bird. This was a very large Iceland falcon, so large indeed that at first it was taken for a female or immature snowy owl. A few minutes later, and quite close, a much smaller and darker Iceland falcon, mobbed by arctic terns, flew out from behind the hill, but not towards the geese. This no doubt was the tiercel, the male. The falcon, the female, out on the marsh beyond, paid no attention to him. The whole behaviour of the geese was strange and it may be that the presence of the hawks had something to do with it.

We trotted home well pleased with our great success and arrived at camp just in time for the 10.0 p.m. radio sked. Communication was good, and we got a correct text for British Minister Jack Greenway's message of 23rd handed in at 17.23:

> "*Much regret due mistake in London Sunderland pilot received no instructions re dropping. Am telegraphing London ensure these issued for return flight approximately four days' time. Please give exact map reference of your position. Greenway.*"

We passed our position at 64° 33′ N., 18° 47′ W. on west bank of Þjórsá, which he received O.K.

Then over supper the others retailed the great doings of the day to poor James, who had missed them, and went finally to bed exhausted. Phil had handled every one of the 247 struggling, flapping, kicking, scratching geese, no mean feat for a girl.

CHAPTER XIII

Peter's Diary: Netting, Botany and an Air-drop

" *Thurs. 26 July.* A wonderful hot sunny morning. While Valli was bringing the horses I went down to photograph the gentians (*G. nivalis*) and *Veronica fruticans* on the river-bank, sunbathing without shirt the while. As we set off southward down the river-bank, thin cloud came up high, but it was a warm and delightful day—and a long one. We left camp at 12.30 and arrived back at 9.15 p.m., nearly nine hours in the saddle. The first geese we saw—over fifty of them—ran down into the Þjórsá and across it.

" Farther down, near where we tagged two cygnets, and near also to a curious curved stone, like a seated figure, a kind of " Penseur " of the Þjórsá, we came upon three or four families of geese and caught one adult and three goslings. This hunt was interesting if disappointing. We surrounded the birds successfully—about twenty of them—but instead of clustering they spread out on the top of the rocky mound and crouched. Then, one or two at a time, they broke out. Eventually, when the bunching plan was evidently a failure, we fell to hunting individuals and only got four. I was hurtling about among the big stones in ordinary shoes, and realised the danger of sharing James's fate. It would be so easy to turn a second ankle and disastrously reduce the operational efficiency. It is bad enough being one short.

"Considering carefully why we were unable to round up this bunch of geese, we believe that the chief reason was that we first appeared too close to them, and that, when suddenly very hard pressed, the idea of individual escape, including crouching, becomes uppermost in the goose mind. If driven from a considerable distance, flock cohesion is established. Thus the two influences are (1) the safety of being in a crowd, (2) panic, scatter, every goose for himself. It is important to maintain (1) and avoid (2). (1) is difficult to re-establish once lost, and is easier the larger the number of geese.

"Just before reaching the mouth of the Hnífá we divided, Phil and Finnur going along behind the hill over which the first pinkfeet goslings of the trip ran as we were coming up. The lake from which they then ran, however, was now dried up. Meanwhile Valli and I saw a small party of geese down on the marsh at the Hnífá mouth. I thought they were too near the treacherous sands and the river, but Valli went off, and had a wonderful gallop over hard black sand, eventually returning driving in front of him four large goslings. He caught three, and Phil, having arrived from the hills, caught the fourth. Later Valli caught a fifth, and, having ringed them, we repaired to a rather decorative moss-fringed spring for lunch. We decided to follow the river on down towards Eyvafen, and we drove a party of about fifty geese down the middle of the Þjórsá ahead of us. Over a brow of green in Eyvafen we came on fifty geese which may well have been the same. It was good galloping and Phil and Valli got round them. Many, including adults, crouched, and when I came up from the Eyvafenskvísl side there was a stony patch with four adults and one gosling crouching on it. Valli and Phil were still on their horses, standing, and I could see a bunch of geese between them. I tried to pick up the adults, creeping up to them in the approved style, but they all broke before I reached them, and I finally got the gosling which, contrary to usual form, remained crouching until I got my net on to it. Then I came up to the goslings (with one adult) which were bunched between Phil and Valli. Unfortunately we could not maintain equilibrium. In one dart the adult became detached and was lost, and before we got them bunched again the number had fallen to sixteen. Now Valli got out the nets and set up a V with the stakes, about ten yards long. This took about twenty minutes, during which the goslings (one ringed one among them) sat about. Some of them fed. They became perfectly used to our presence. Occasionally one would wander away from the flock, half crouched, and when headed would sit down as if to crouch. This particularly applied to one of three very large ones, almost able to fly. At last Valli was ready and we edged the birds down into a hollow, where the net was staked out. The adventurous large gosling made one interesting and very determined attempt to break out between Phil and me. When this was defeated it ran back to the flock almost gratefully.

"We got them into the net successfully, but one of these large birds climbed over where it was low—over the backs of the others—and got out. I gave chase (flushing a young ptarmigan, of a brood which Finnur had already seen), but with these almost flying goslings it is quite useless. I could make no impression on it at all, and having run 50 yards I gave up and came back to help the rest. We ringed fifteen and recorded the recapture of 21028, ringed eleven days before in the little valley next to our camp (James calls it Failure Creek).

When we had packed up and were ready to go on, I looked across to Kerlingarfjöll, which was very clear and beautiful. What a setting for these lovely birds! What a wonderful background for all the exciting things we are seeing and doing! Phil and I stood for a while absorbing the beauty and grandeur of it. We were actively enjoying that particular aspect of our trip, that our scientific work, that all our endeavour and effort should be happening in the middle of these glorious mountains and glaciers. We felt at that moment very lucky and happy.

We passed the remains of an adult pre-moult goose, picked clean perhaps by some large predatory bird—eagle, falcon or owl—or perhaps by skuas, or gulls. We had decided to look over the next ridge and then to turn for home. As we came to the crest Valli suddenly dipped his head and turned back. There were geese on the other side and he thought we should set the nets. I went carefully on foot to the crest and saw about sixty geese undisturbed, sitting on a green *Salix* ridge beyond. They were three hundred yards away. We selected a hillock of stones and gravel on our side of the ridge and set up the nets there. It took three-quarters of an hour and we made a proper job of it—clove hitches top and bottom on all the stakes. For stakes we are using the uprights of the Eric Hosking hides—those not being used as wireless mast and handles for hand-nets—some of the greenheart sticks and the poles of the clap net cut in half. We had the one long rabbit net, about ninety yards, which gave a cage and two thirty-five-yard wings.

" As soon as it was finished Valli and I set off to go round by the river and get behind the geese, while Finnur and Phil flanked them in. As we came down to the river's edge thirty geese went off the bank into the water. Valli and I went on round, and found more geese on the river-bank where it curved to the right, but suddenly there was a row of heads quite close looking over at us from the top of the greensward. I topped the bank to find them curling back to the right across my tracks to the river. Sörli, my horse, was reluctantly persuaded into a gallop and we headed them off. Meanwhile a nice lot of geese were going up ahead of Valli. It looked as though at least sixty, perhaps a hundred, geese were going forward, and already I could see some of them pausing on the crest of the ridge, fifty or sixty yards short of the net. Then suddenly they began to crouch. We were hustling them too fast. One crouched on the slope and I tried to start it on, but it broke back to the river. This was the pattern. At the crest many were crouching and although some had gone forward it was terribly difficult to get the crouched birds to set off in the right direction. On the far side of the net a sad misunderstanding had come into play, largely due to a lack of knowledge of the terrain. Phil had ridden so far up the ridge to head off a possible early exodus that she couldn't get back to watch her flank of the net, and a good many birds slipped through. But most crouched and broke back. In the end we had sixteen birds in the net, including only three adults. We got these into sacks and later Finnur brought in one more gosling, which we drove into the net for ease and certainty of capture.

"Valli said that a rather large flock of geese had escaped at the south end and that it was still worth trying to get them in by a second drive. I had no faith in this, but thought they might pick up one or two lost goslings. So Phil and Valli went off again. But the operation was abortive.

"So we ringed the birds, took up the nets and rode home. It was 7.45 p.m., and we reached camp at 9.15. Soon after crossing Eyvafenskvísl, Valli, who was riding across the mouth of a small stream out on the sand, got his horse badly bogged. He stayed on and the horse got itself out by an extraordinary series of jumps with both front feet going together, then both hind. It was the worst place we have come upon so far. We returned by way of the bottom of Hnífárver and through the Hnífá arm of Tjarnarver. We found no geese at all but two pairs of swans with young, both in the marshes where we had found them earlier, and all their cygnets supposedly tagged. The first pair had three and were still in the Hnífá arm, and the second pair had two, and were back in Chipping Swanmarsh ; and were therefore presumably the chipping swans. This attachment for the territory even after hatching is interesting and in direct contrast (apparently) to the geese, which seem to wander in bunches far from their original nesting area.

" During the ride we saw our first young golden plover.

" Back at camp we had admirable radio contact. No news of this aircraft which has been imminent now for well over a week. It is almost too late for it to be worth while at all, except that I really do need more films badly. To this end, and to remind Jack Greenway, we sent him the following message :

' *Movie films urgently needed, hope they have arrived and can be dropped. Scott.*'

" We were all very tired in the evening. Finnur was telling fascinating tales of the eruption of Hekla and of an earthquake at Reykjanes which threw him to the ground, and how he tried to hold on to something but could find nothing firm, and how the ground was going up and down. He imitated the awful hissing noise which preceded the 'quake.

" There was a stupendous red sunset, reflected pinkly off the Tungnafellsjökull. It was a warm night.

" *Fri. 27 July.* A rest day for the ponies, fine but with a cool north wind. James's ankle still pretty swollen and very black and blue. I rebandaged it for him. Finnur is skinning the casualties among the goslings. There are three good skins. The rest will provide crop contents and we shall eat them tonight. They should be nice and tender.

" Phil and I have been sunbathing in a sun-trap we have found in the deep cleft of the little iron stream. Here on a verdant bank with glorious deep blue gentians all round us, it is deliciously warm.

" James has been working hard on the figures of our recaptures, using them in an effort to determine the numbers of geese here, and hence the numbers of breeding pairs (see Appendix E, p. 223).

" Radio contact quite good tonight, but no messages. We got a time signal, however. Having lost the winder of my watch I cannot correct it. Being self-winding it continues to go, but I have to make a ten-minute correction and in another week it will be much more. Still no news of this aircraft. I should not care if I did not need the film so badly. I now have about 70 feet left, having used 2,100.

" *Sat. 28 July.* A very exciting day. It was clear and bright and sunny, with a high barometer but a cold north wind, blowing quite hard. We got away at 10.45 for a netting expedition—to fish the nets on the north crest of Oddkelsalda and then go on and set a net on Arnarfellsalda.

" Our plan for the first drive was almost the same as the last time with only minor modification, to allow me to get round ahead of Finnur and prevent the geese on the W. side of the crest from going into the Miklakvísl. We have planned these drives with some precision, with a sketch map and each person's position at various times after the split-up across Blautakvísl—which is H hour. I was to be at Miklakvísl by H plus 1 hr. 5 mins. and at the corner of Falcon Marsh by H+1.20, which was Valli's emerging time.

" Finnur and I saw no geese whatever on our side of the net hill—the only thing of interest we saw was the tiercel Iceland falcon being mobbed by a pair of arctic skuas. The trio flew right over our heads. Also we passed a brood of fledged purple sandpipers. The area seemed to be deserted of geese except that I could see some round and beyond Illaversalda. I quite expected that the drive would be a failure. However, when Valli started across the marsh I soon saw that a goodly bunch of geese was coming ahead of him, and after them a second bunch. For a moment I missed the second lot, thinking that I must have been mistaken and seen only the spray breaking at the lee side of one of the lakes, but then they reappeared and I headed them up the hill. One or two tried to break down the ridge to Miklakvísl and I rather think a few got through. But Sörli was in great form, and we galloped over the grassy ridge in zigzags and even circles, rounding up every last goose.

" On the top we took a goodly bunch of geese into the cage and closed the door. Phil and I thought there must be at least sixty birds—actually there were 97, including twenty-three adults. Seventeen of them were recaptured (one a tag), eleven (all goslings) from the previous big catch.

" We had completed the ringing by about 1.30 and went across Miklakvísl, saving the life of a gosling (2772) which had been attacked and wounded by a great black-backed gull, and on to the outfall of Vallarvatn, where Finnur had lost his egg micrometer, measuring a dunlin's eggs. Here we had lunch and hunted for the instrument in vain. Nearby we saw a just-fledged baby dunlin.

" We had earlier seen a good many geese going over the ridge of Arnarfellsalda, and after lunch we slanted up the west side, and then I went ahead to spy. There were quite a good number—say two hundred in the marsh beyond the hill—and it certainly seemed worth setting the net. This was the single 90-yard rabbit net which we had taken up from the long wing on Oddkelsalda after the big catch on 25th.

" While I was spying I suddenly saw the head of a goose about fifty yards away, and a whole group of about thirty came up the ridge towards the summit. They saw me, but without being greatly alarmed, and moved up the hill away from me. I went over the crest of the ridge to spy the east side of the Wave. Here the marsh was empty. Clearly the thing to do was to retreat from the west side, round the south to the east, where a covered approach could be made to the very summit itself.

" This we did—I leading on foot. Down in the marsh below us the cygnets, which we had always failed to tag, were reduced from five to four. We set up the nets fairly quickly, and then, after pointing out the geese to Valli, who was full of scepticism, we put the plan into action. Finnur was also sceptical, but he explained to Valli with great enthusiasm that although he could only see about twenty geese there were hundreds in the dead ground below us and much nearer. I fervently prayed there would be, and when the time came there were.

"Valli was to follow the course of the Innri Múlakvísl out for a distance to be left to his discretion, and Phil was to go out to the eastward, making a sort of pincer movement round the marshes and slopes on the north face of the Wave. Finnur was to mark the east flank of the net, I the west.

"My side was very steep and would, I soon realised, be up fairly easy. I watched Valli, a tiny equestrian dot, riding the little river's edge. At one point he passed close to some geese which did not see him because of the high banks. These geese threatened to break out behind him, so I came down from the hill to head them back. This I succeeded in doing, but before I could get back to the top of the hill again a few geese had by-passed the net and were going on down the ridge. Apparently at this time Finnur was having a desperate job covering rather a large frontage of the slope down which the geese were making determined efforts to escape.

"However, there were still a good lot of geese on the top. Finnur's horse and the pack horse were at the back of the cage and had already turned some geese back down the ridge. I tried to stop them but in vain. However, they were heading for Valli and Phil, so it did not matter much. I dismounted and led the two horses across to my flank. Meanwhile the main crowd of geese was slowed up on the first crest of the hill about a hundred and fifty yards short of the net. Valli was coming across the marsh and I waved him round behind them. At last we had a splendid bunch in the V of the net, and I filmed them as they filed into the cage. I thought there were over two hundred but actually there were only 180. As we were closing in on them one bird resolutely turned and ran out almost able to fly. Presently a second did the same thing. This one got the strong wind under it and rose quite high above us, flapping nineteen to the dozen.

"We pulled one wing of the net across to act as a door. It was after 8.0 p.m. when we had finished the job of ringing. Two goslings had hanged themselves. There were six recaptures and 172 were newly ringed.

"The wind had fallen away and it was a marvellously clear evening. Hekla, eighty miles away, looked quite close. We rode home very fast in order to get back for the 10 p.m. radio sked, for although James could have listened for messages he could not have answered, nor, without a watch, would he have known when to listen.

"We trotted fast all the way, even cantered at times: and all this in order to get news of this aircraft and my film—news from Reykjavík to Bólstaður instead of Aix to Ghent. And at the end of it all radio contact was very poor; we got only a time signal from him, and he was unable to read us at all. James reports that his ankle is better, but it's still pretty swollen. He has been wonderfully good about it.

"*Sun. 29 July.* A fine day with high cloud and warm; a day with a botanical objective. James is still incapacitated, but the rest of us planned to climb Ólafsfell, one of the mountain bastions holding in the Hofsjökull. It was a long ride to the foot of it, by way of Nautalda and Nauthagi, and a subsidiary object was to collect fresh algae from the hot springs and record the exact temperatures, which we had not been able to do on the previous visit. We passed a brood of eleven ptarmigan poults with *both* parents in attendance.

"The ride across Tjarnarver was quite expeditious. Only once, when we came upon about a hundred geese, the nearest of them about a hundred yards away, were we unable to resist a hunt. But the young birds are so much larger and faster now, and the old ones are growing their primaries and no longer crouch so well. So we caught only four—two adults and two goslings. However, the whole operation did not delay us more than ten minutes at the outside. There were a hundred more geese near Ptarmigan Lake.

" We rode on to Nautalda and over Miklakvísl to Nauthagi, without further incident (except for the finding of a very old and small goose-fold in an extraordinary place, on a stony ridge, so low that it was barely raised above the shingle beds at the foot of Nautalda on the south side). At Nauthagi we had lunch and afterwards caught sticklebacks in water at 29° C., found new plants—notably the tiny three-petalled *Ranunculus reptans*—and caught an insect running round the sides of the oozing hot springs (*Salda littoralis*, so Finnur says). I think it must be one of the bugs (Hemiptera). We also mapped the springs and took temperature readings in each, and collected algae in some. In one there was a network of what looked like cobwebs. I think it was an alga with some deposit from the hot water, perhaps silica or a sulphurous substance. We collected some of it.

" We saw a new bird for the area—a redshank. Later we saw it in a hot pool. It had a downy head and was evidently a this year's baby, but it flew quite well, so we do not think it was hatched there. We also found a second hatched goose-nest among the hot springs.

" From Nauthagi we rode to the foot of Ólafsfell (where on the first foot-hill we found another goose nest of this year). It was a long climb up a bare forbidding slope. We led our horses, who hated it. Gradually, below us, unfolded the most marvellous view. At first we looked down on our right on the tongue of the glacier and the source of one part of the Miklakvísl. It ran out from under the ice by way of a spectacular cleft, above which was an ice bridge and then a curious oval hole through which the river could be seen running down, milky brown.

9*a*. *A tongue of the Hofsjökull Icecap from Ólafsfell.* (P.T.-P.)
b. *The foot of the receding glacier with one of the many tributaries of the Þjórsá.* (P.T.-P.)

"We paused on a high shoulder and looked back. Below the whole oasis of Þjórsárver was spread out. Heavy rain was softening the outlines of the Hágangas, Nyrðri-Háganga and

SKETCH MAP OF HOT SPRINGS AT NAUTHAGI

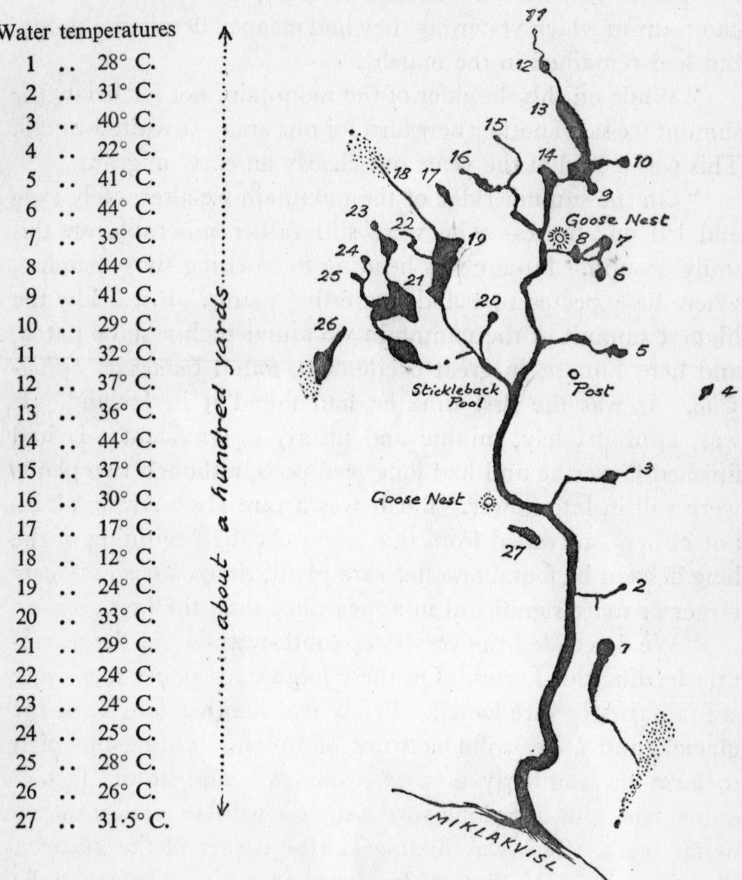

Syðri-Háganga (pronounced Howgunger), the twin mountain lumps which lie between us and the Vatnajökull. To the south, towards our camp, the weather was bright so that the lakes and rivers shone out silver.

"Oddkelsver was full of small lakes, and so was the island of Tjarnarver between the two channels of the Blautakvísl. Away in the distance about $7\frac{1}{2}$ miles away I could see the camp quite clearly in the binoculars, and could also see the two ponies we had left behind, still in the little enclosure near camp (from which yesterday they had escaped despite hobbling, but had remained in the marsh).

"While on this shoulder of the mountain, not far below the summit we saw another new bird for our area—a white wagtail. This was a bird of the year, but clearly an early migrant.

"On the summit ridge of the mountain we alternately rode and led our horses—who were still rather miserable on this stony ground. Finnur was heading for melting snow patches, where he expected new and interesting plants. Just below the highest summit of the mountain we found such a snow patch, and here Finnur, in great excitement, found *Cardamine bellidifolia*. It was the first time he had found it in Iceland. It was, appropriately, minute and utterly insignificant. It had finished flowering and had long seed pods, although two plants were still in late flower. But it was a rare High Arctic plant, not hitherto recorded from this area. At the beginning of the long descent he found another rare plant, *Arabis alpina*, scarcely larger or more significant in appearance than the first.

"We descended the very steep south-west face of the mountain leading our horses. On these loose scree slopes they were still amazingly sure-footed. Below was another tongue of the glacier, and a beautiful network of streams leading out of it to form the southerly area of Miklakvísl, and at the foot of our almost cliff-like slope was a stream with vegetation along its far bank. This was Jökulkriki (the corner of the glacier). Pl. 16, p. 189. Valli took his two horses down into a gully full of snow. I took Sörli down that way too. The snow was easier on the horses' hooves. It was very steep and I more or less skated down, ending with an almost uncontrolled run over a harder, more frozen bit at the bottom. Sörli skated with me, a very creditable display of pair skating (though perhaps no more than might be expected from a one-time winner of a junior pair-skating Championship !). Phil followed with Hetja. Her boot-soles were smoother and she had less control until she crouched down and began to ski. This effective glissade brought her to the bottom of the slope undamaged.

" From here we rode along the foot of the mountain to another hot spring. This welled up at the edge of the gravel of the spring glacier torrent. There were about three springs, round which the pebbles were whitened, and a cloud of steam was blowing away from each. These springs were much hotter than Nauthagi (62° C. instead of 44°). One could not bear one's hands in the water at the source, but we dabbled in it a few feet away, warming our extremities by standing in the stream in our rubber boots while soaking our hands. We took a sample of the algae at 52°—the hottest in which they seem to be able to grow. The growth was richer and greener and more luscious at temperatures around 35°-40°. Finnur found a few new plants, but the vegetation was scanty because the gravel was evidently covered by the river at peak flood time. There was a dwarf growth of a species of *Juncus* (probably *J. articulatus*) and also *Sagina* sp. and *Epilobium* sp. *Saxifraga oppositifolia* was flowering there, but not in the hot spot. This was surprising because it is long over in most places.

" Our return route was round the west side of the marsh behind Nautalda. As we crossed a soft part of the stony river bed, the stones moss-covered with a fairly rich growth of *Saxifraga hirculus*, we disturbed a pair of purple sandpipers. They began injury-feigning, and then I saw a small chick. After a long run, during which the female sandpiper flopped and dithered in front of me within four or five feet, I caught the downy. The mother went off in a brilliant rodent-run, accompanied by a shrill squeal, exactly like a rat, and totally unrelated to any call of the bird. As in the case of the dunlin some weeks ago, I was once more immensely impressed with this extraordinary behaviour, and by thoughts of its evolution. The chick, as is usual with tiny waders, was a creature of great beauty: rich purplish-brown and black dotted with white, so that the result is unbelievably moss-like. We photographed him and then returned him to his anxious parents. As we rode on, one parent continued to lead ahead of us, as we discussed the whole astonishing phenomenon.

"On the east side of Söðulfell (Saddle hill) we came upon an area of lava and a small crater, not marked on the map. We also found perhaps a hundred and fifty geese in the attractive system of little marshes and pools at the south-east corner of this mountain. It was into these marshes that we had seen the geese pouring from Nautalda on 15 July.

"From here we returned home almost without incident, except for a fly which flew into my eye—they had been intermittently troublesome all day—and the important discovery, based on instructions by Phil, that my horse could be persuaded to tripple instead of trotting if I kept the reins tight enough and managed to get across to him the fact that this did not mean he was to stop. This discovery greatly added to the comfort of the return journey.

"In Pintail Marsh we surveyed what seems to be an ideal camp site. It would be very good, I think, if, as we are planning, we return here with improved equipment and a rather larger party in the summer of 1953.

"A fine red sunset out of a cloudy sky, and James waiting for us with the steak-and-kidney pudding a-brewing. He had put it on when he saw a pair of swans come over the hill (the pair from Deserted Swanmarsh) evidently, he judged, put up by us. Radio had been no good at 10.0 (we weren't back till 10.30) because the receiver had been left on for 24 hours and was dead. Finnur was the culprit this time—I having done it last time.

"Geese ringed: 2 ad. 2 juv. Total 4, grand total marked: 866 (250 ad.).

"*Mon. 30 July.* A rest day, with continuous rain from soon after midday. Finnur has been pressing his flowers. James is making his sketch map from the air photographs, and I have been writing up the ring records and this journal. We have 185 rings left. A white wagtail has been chirruping outside the tent—perhaps several of them.

"At about 6.0 p.m. we heard the Catalina returning from Seyðisfjördur—we had heard it going in the morning. Phil saw it through the crack in the tent door. It was much lower than usual. Then it turned sharply. Could it be looking for our camp? It turned away, then back again, and passed far to the west; then suddenly it turned in again towards us, losing height. We were ready with cameras as it came straight at the camp. I had one awful moment, when the camera failed, but I had forgotten to wind it. A quick wind, and I was ready for a marvellous shot as it came in. As I panned up on it I saw, in the view-finder, two large sacks come out and drop right in the camp, coming to rest exactly between the three tents. The aircraft circled again and waved to us, and I got another excellent picture of it. Well done, Jack Greenway and the Icelandic air service Flugfélag Íslands! An accurate drop in wretched weather (rain and poor visibility).

"The packages contained the much-needed films—twenty ciné magazines—our mail, with very important items, cans of fruit juice, pâté de foie gras (coals, perhaps, to Newcastle) and newspapers up to 20 July (Icelandic ones later). This was a very exciting affair for us all."

CHAPTER XIV

James's Diary: A Thousand Up

"*31 July.* After breakfast I joined the others and tried my ankle (still slightly swollen) first in a rubber Wellington (it went in) and then on a horse (not so bad). Thought it would hold up for day; it did, reminding me of itself at the start, and when attention was drawn to it by solicitous comrades, and when more than two hours at a stretch riding, and on way home (when I found myself having to look the other way when Peter and Phil were fiddling about with uncatchable geese in their glasses on top of the north crest of Oddkelsalda!). A bumper day and I was very glad to be able to make it, for otherwise I would have missed a proper net-drive.

"*Word-eating department.* I must record that there had been an occasion when I thought that we would have to concentrate on 'pony-hunting' for our main harvest of geese for ringing.

"We first 'drew' the nets on top of the north crest of Oddkelsalda, following the style and plot laid down by several previous attempts. Peter and I on the left wing put a flock off the lake north of Hill 627. They went north into the marsh and we could do nothing with them. But following them a little I found the alleged goose-pen at the N.E. corner of this hill. So that was useful. Peter and Finnur and I continued on to the Miklakvísl via Foxwarren, etc., and met the others eventually at a perfectly blank net. We took it up and carried it with the pack-pony (slightly limping) across the Miklakvísl and had lunch in southern Múlaver, having drawn Illaversalda blank. Wind cold from the north but a fine day, and the wind gradually went down as the day went on. At Arnarfellsalda Valli went right up to the moraine to comb out Múlaver; Phil

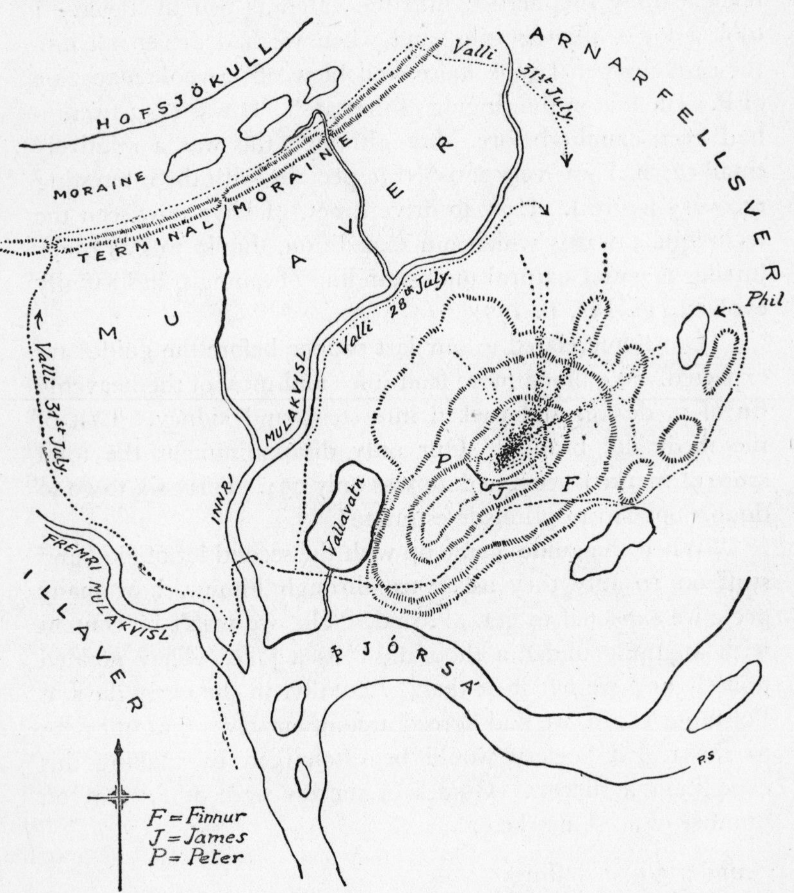

took the east marsh between Arnarfellsalda and the Þjórsá, Peter the west flank, Finnur and I the east flank: James in sight of the east wing of the net, to come up and turn any down-goers. Peter warned me I would hear the geese first, and sure enough I did after about half an hour, turning five or ten that were working out along the net-wing back, and coming up on Phil's call in time to see and photograph two small herds, one mainly of adults, the other mainly of young, being calmly shepherded into the catching-pen by Peter. I took a lot of photographs, and when we had driven all into the catching-pen I took more, and blew off a whole magazine of P.'s cinema on the ringing of the catch. It was 114; twenty-had been caught before. But although this was a relatively small catch, I was very satisfied (especially with the interesting recovery figures). How to drive a net. I have now seen the technique towards which our expedition, thanks to P.'s quick intelligence and natural understanding of animals, has rapidly evolved (Pl. 12*b*, p. 177).

"Got home elated to our last supper before the guides are expected. We blued more fruit juice and most of the heavenly tin of p. de f.g. and tucked into steak and kidney. Last of the medicinal brandy. Our only disappointment the total score of marked geese to date was only 954. Forty-six to go to double our most optimistic estimate!

"When the guides came up with the second lot of food and stuff on 10 July they asked us, through Finnur, how many geese we expected to get. P. said, "Oh, we won't be content with anything under a thousand" as a joke. They nodded politely and we left it at that. Actually, in the early days at Bólstaður camp, we had agreed among ourselves that our debt to the Royal Society would be discharged by making this expedition a success. Guides of success were as follows, on number of geese marked:

under 50	failure
100	satisfactory
200	success
500	roaring success

Roaring was the word. So far we are screaming. Are we to

finish here? Peter makes plans for a visit to Eyvafen tomorrow to catch the elusive forty-six.

"Receiver still useless, but we pass a message to Gufunes that we hope to be out on 5 or 6 August.

"*1 August.* It was a silent windless fairly sunny morning, after a still warm night. We didn't have to go more than two kilometres from camp, on the way to Eyvafen, for the missing 46. Indeed, we were ringing so many geese on what we now call Round-up Hill in Lower Tjarnarver that the expected guides, arriving from Kjálkaver round about 13.00, found us still engaged with the remnants of goslings in the catching-pen, and stood amusedly by while the ponies sniffed and blew at each other. So we returned to camp a triumphant convoy of seven humans and eighteen horses, with a specially warm feeling promoted by having, in our first visit to what are now going to become the famous goose-grounds of the Þjórsá, marked no less than 1,151 geese (382 adults, 769 goslings) and recovered two marked in the previous winter in Britain. Just as we reached camp it began to rain from a calm sky—a cosy kind of rain. We had a meal with the guides and counted our blessings, and felt really elated and satisfied.

"What happened at the hunt was this. Arriving at the bottom right-hand corner of Peter's sketch-map, I saw some geese (from horseback) pushing up to the red-throated diver lakes (top right-hand corner); they had seen us. We were discussing whether to lay on a drive, and I had just suggested that there might be others in the bog, when Phil drew our attention to a big lot going along the marsh away from us, south-west. At once the shape of the drive became clear, and it needed no orders for Valli to rush on, and the rest of us to follow. The grey stony hill, Round-up Hill, was jam to cover, for Finnur and I could get into position without being seen by the geese. Valli and Phil got most of them moving uphill, Peter saw them arrive there in time to urge me into a more southerly position, and I breasted a rise in the grey hill, on my pony, to find myself facing what I thought to be 180 geese (they afterwards turned out to be 206—202 caught, 2 goslings escaped from the pen, 2 adults flew). I just managed to close with Finnur enough to prevent a Þjórsá-wards trickle, led by an old gander, from developing into a pipe-off.

"The goose-pack bunched at the highest point of the hill. The bunchers changed a bit at first; to begin with Finnur and me on the Þjórsá side and Peter to the north-east. Then Valli quickly unloaded the nets on to the ground from the pack pony, which he had taken over from Finnur, and Finnur moved round to the west side, Valli taking his place on the south-east side. Peter called Phil to the job of making a net-pen and wings, which she did, single-handed, in under half an hour, in spite of snagged poles and tangled nets. It was amazing how well she sorted it all out and got it up, right and good and stone-loaded. But we had to keep the geese entertained for half an hour. All the time it seemed to me that they were trying to get into the Þjórsá—that is, past me, as I stood on my pony between them and it. Led by two big ganders—one at each end of the flock, and either or both of which I would cheerfully have shot—slide movements began, sometimes into the gap between me and Valli, sometimes between Peter and me. These were easy to check so long as there was only one at a time; a few steps of my horse to one side or the other was all that was necessary. But when such a movement started at each end simultaneously it was necessary to decide on one end and call a neighbour to cover the other. We all suffered from anxiety-neurosis. I had persistent exchange with Finnur about whether he was near enough. Valli kept taking his eyes off the geese to watch how Phil (behind him) was getting on with the net. But we held them quiet, in spite of the ganders, though these began to get very bold at the end, and once I thought they had nearly gone between me and Valli. The flock clucked and piped all the time, and when the adult cackling got loud we knew nonsense was brewing, and that an assault was coming.

"At last Phil said she had the nets ready, and Valli relaxed his pressure. One of the ganders made a break immediately, bashed over the wing of the net where it was too low, and disclosed itself as airborne (but only just). Phil, who had retired a bit, came in again to put in a new stake, and once more we niggled the flock along to the net. And this time they went in in classic style—straight and not too fast—and Valli came across with the short wing to close it, and our geese were penned.

"Usual routine followed. Phil and Valli (after the latter

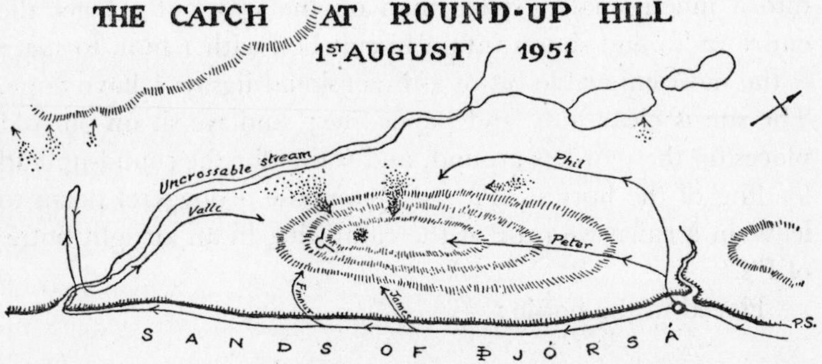

had been off to settle the horses) fishing out geese (first) and goslings (mostly later). Finnur writing down. I was rescuing choking goslings with heads twisted in the net (we lost none this time) and adjusting goose-pressure in the pen. Peter ringing, and when we had run out of all the rings we had brought, tagging. I relaxed for a bit after an hour, to rest my ankle, and took some colour photos of the doings. Peter got some wonderful ciné-shots of this herd and its entry into the net. A classic operation. All we lost were two goslings which got through holes in the net and two adults which flew from the flock. After we had ringed them, several other adults disclosed that they could fly. Hooray for the Last Round-Up!

"The guides who have come up are our friends Snjólfur (from the first journey) and Ágúst (of the relief on 10 July). Both seem cheerful and have a fine lot of horses. We are back in camp with them for lunch and spend the rest of the day packing and collecting ourselves. It rains and drizzles but gets drier towards nightfall, so there is a decent prospect of packing dry tents.

"*2 August.* Get up at eight. Dry tents. Everything packed by 11.30, and immense bonfire roars for half an hour aided by five gallons of surplus paraffin. We leave eight ration packs in the *kofi* against our next expedition, but particularly as they are two pony-power that we cannot spare. Everything goes into a much smaller space than on the way out; I get the entire radio and spares into a biscuit box with 1 mm. to spare—the most enjoyable bit of 3-dimensional jigsaw I have done. The site is clear, tidy and paper-free; and we sit on our old places on the tent-less ground, and wait—for the round-up and loading of the horses. P. and I compose a doggerel poem to leave in a cairn we raise at the camp-site, in an airtight bottle of F's.

Placed in the bottle:

"*THE SEVERN WILDFOWL TRUST EXPEDITION*

camped here from 26 June-2 August 1951.
Its object was to mark Pink-footed Geese.
1,151 geese were caught and marked with rings and tags.

For six long weeks we've drunk our fill
Of the beautiful slope of Buttercup Hill,
Of the lush green marshes of Tjarnarver
And the wild grey geese who are breeding there.
For six long weeks we have lived—and now
We must take our leave of the wide Þjórsá.

(PS)

But back at home on a winter's night
When we hear the beat of the goosewing flight,
When we hear the cry of the pinkfoot gander
On Tay and Solway and where they wander,
We'll think of the ice-cap, and Arnarfell
And the Þjórsárver that we love so well.

(JF)

Signed by all, incl. Valli."

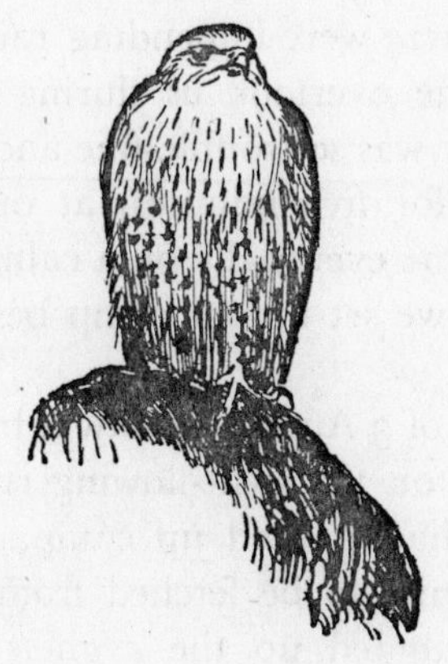

Iceland Falcon

CHAPTER XV

Journey Home

EVENTUALLY at 15.30 on 2 August we took our last look at Bólstaður. There were impending rain storms about, but only one minor one overtook us during the crossing of the desert; the journey was so trouble-free and quick that we only rested the horses, for five minutes, at our old camp-site at Kjálkaver. We came eventually on a calm fine evening to the river Dalsá, where we set up our camp beside a newly rebuilt *kofi*.

In the morning of 3 August we saw a brood of four cygnets with their parents, on the swift-flowing river (a very unusual place). After we had packed up camp, and while we were waiting for the ponies to be fetched from Loðnaver, half an hour away, we rounded up the cygnets and tagged them. This took an hour at least, and we finished up with a good many boots full of water. The cob was still full-winged but the pen was moulted; an interesting differentiation which had not been recorded before, so far as we knew. The only flightless swans we had seen to this date had been females. We saw goose-droppings on a little islet in the Dalsá; some were of goslings, thus proving that the geese we had seen there on the way up were in fact breeding.

At Starkaðsver, where we stopped for a picnic lunch at about 6.30, one of the ponies was taken ill. It was a pathetic sight, unable to feed, sitting or lying. We had to take it on unloaded, which meant that one of the guides had to walk. Snjólfur rode it across the rivers bareback and without a bridle, though once he threaded a piece of string through its mouth.

We saw no geese on the journey until we came to Skúmstungur at the junction of the Tungnaá and Þjórsá. Here we had seen our first goslings on the upward journey, and had identified them rather uncertainly as grey lags; this time all were pinkfeet, about five families. We climbed over Sandafell and trotted down the other side to Hólaskógur, the site of our first camp. We arrived ten minutes ahead of the pack train and sat watching a red sunset reflected on the lower slopes of cloud-topped Hekla across the Þjórsá. It had been a nine-and-a-half-hour ride, and we had done in two days a journey which had taken three on the way out.

The next day we had a four to five hour ride to Ásólfsstaðir and civilisation. The way led through the famous beauty-spot Gjáin, and here we diverged to the lip of the gorge of the Rauðá, a bowl with many mossy banks and caves and springs and hollows and a flying foss (waterfall). We crossed a bed of boulders and the river lower down, to mount a grassy slope to Stöng, the saga-age farm of Gaukur Trandilsson, the chief of the Þjórsárdalur in the saga age; the farm was buried by an eruption of Hekla, probably that of 1104. It was the largest of sixteen farms in the valley (all subsequently deserted because of the ash) from which undoubtedly the operators of some of the goose-folds which the expedition found must have started out each year. Nothing is written of the geese in the sagas, but they contain little of such details, even in other areas where, for example, fishing and sheep-farming thrived, but where fish and sheep are scarcely mentioned.

The farm consisted of a large hall, in which there was a central fire marked out by stones, and an inner chamber, also with a central fire. These and two chambers opening off them, one of them a larder with a round space for the vat containing *skyr* (sour milk), were enclosed by a turf wall on a foundation of lava blocks. In separate buildings were the cow-byre, with stalls for sixteen cows, and the forge, with anvil and trough—both of stone. But the most interesting part of the house was a channelled building, which might have been a cold store, where the meat could be hung over ice-filled grooves; perhaps this is where they kept their goslings on ice.

We could not help imagining the return of the goose-catchers to this farm, their ponies laden with geese and goslings for smoking or salting for winter food. They knew about the north crest of Oddkelsalda, and the flat top of Arnarfellsalda; they knew about the pinkfeet, about their behaviour when flightless; they knew what we now knew about how to drive them on to the hill tops. We saluted the pioneers.

Down the road which led along the arid valley we caught up with the pack train. We passed numbers of cars and jeeps, all of which stopped to let the ponies go by. After resting the horses for a few minutes on a lush green shelf at the side of the valley we came round the corner of the hill, and there was the neat white farmstead of Ásólfsstaðir, set in the beautiful green meadows with a frame of hills and birch woods. Beside the big barn we dismounted for the last time and unloaded the pack ponies.

The farm was full of tourists, so we had to camp that night—which was as well, for the tents were wet. We had an excellent meal, said goodbye to Valli, Ágúst and Snjólfur, and slept late the next morning.

We were packed up and ready to leave after lunch by the milk truck (which had seats in front); the heavy luggage was to follow by lorry. There were last-minute claims of additional expense, which were finally settled amicably, and Jóhann took over three ration boxes as gratuity. So, in rather a rush, we left Ásólfur's lovely farm, with its bevies of children, its ponies and cows, its tame lamb (now with well-grown horns), its black dog with a white cravat, its picturesque old grandmother in traditional black dress and lace, its old gaffer (who had

12*a*. *About 300 Pinkfoot goslings and flightless adults rounded up on the North Crest of Oddkelsalda, 25 July 1951.* (F.G.)

b. *A catch of 114 Pinkfeet at the summit of Arnarfellsalda on 31 July 1951.* (J.F.)

spent two summers on the moraine and seen snowy owls there frequently), with its tractor and jeep and farm machinery and all its untidy friendliness.

And so down the valley to Sellfoss for tea, and Reykjavík thereafter, by way of the hot springs and greenhouses of Reykir.

Monday 6 August was spent mostly in the garden of the Minister's residence, where we sunbathed in near-tropical heat and read our mail. In the afternoon we forgathered at the Museum, and later with Finnur's wife Guðríður dined at the Borg and danced a little.

Peter's diary for 7 August provides the ending of the expedition:

" Another brilliant hot day full of hasty and last-minute arrangements. Up at 6.0 to be at the airport at 7.0 in order to buy James's air-ticket. He left at 8.0, for London, flown by Þórsteinn Jónsson—Tony Jónsson, ex-R.A.F., who had come over on the plane with us in June, and had flown James over St. Kilda two years ago.

" A hectic morning—haircut, buy ring, cash cheques, hold press conference at Museum. Lunch at the Legation and at 2.45 an assembly of Legation staff, plus Finnur and his wife, and nice Americans — Hughes — to watch His Britannic Majesty's Minister marry Phil and me. Jack Greenway did it beautifully, and afterwards there was champagne and a lovely cake specially made by his friendly housekeeper. Bryan Holt, Irish, with an Icelandic wife, who has been in Iceland for three years and speaks the language fluently, produced the ring and thus qualified as best man. Finnur gave Phil away and was first witness. Peter Lake, First Secretary, was the other. We took photographs and films in glorious sunshine on the steps of the Legation and on the grass ' round-about ' of the drive.

" Afterwards a new passport photograph for Phil and then to the airport—to take off at 5.30 in a Catalina flying-boat for

Akureyri and later Mývatn. The pilot of this plane was the one who had dropped the bags at our camp.

"He was not sure if this was the actual plane which dropped them—they have two Catalinas. A delightful flight, part of it spent in the pilot's cockpit—past Langjökull, Eríksjökull, Hofsjökull and Vatnajökull. We saw Hekla, and the Kerlingarfjöll and the Hágangas, and the grey stretch between the last two which contained Þjórsárver, and our familiar lovely places."

CHAPTER XVI

The Last Secrets of the Nesting-places

THIS IS A postscript, summary, envoi—call it what you will, for our expedition is over, and only the stocktaking remains. The measurement of total pinkfoot population is not yet complete, because the passage of two or three years is essential in making the best use of ringing data, and sampling and re-sampling are essential parts of the technique. As this book goes to press the second Severn Wildfowl Trust expedition is setting off for the Þjórsárver—almost exactly two years after the first—in order to sample the pinkfeet again.[1] But recaptures of ringed birds during the intervening winters have given us some idea of total numbers, which the new figures will either confirm or correct, until the truth is finally known.

In October 1951, less than three months after our return from Iceland we caught 530 pinkfeet with our rocket nets in Scotland, of which nine carried rings put on in the Þjórsárver.

[1] Peter returned from this expedition just in time to add this footnote in the last proof stage of a book which perhaps should now be called *The First Thousand Geese*. "The goose-chase in the Þjòrsàrver in 1953 was a success beyond expectation, for by the end of it perhaps one in five of the world pinkfoot population carried a ring. The first big catch of 1953 was on top of Arnarfellsalda—537 on 17 July. On 21 July a party of eight on horse-back drove a big area of the *vers* to the low *alda* at the foot of Hjartarfell: we caught 3,169 geese and goslings! It took just over twelve hours to check and ring them. Afterwards five other important catches were made: 3,115 (also on Arnarfellsalda), 1,892, 1,006, 721 and 695. Altogether 9,005 different geese were caught, though the number of goose-handlings was 12,312. In the catch of 1,892 on 4 August, two days before we left 1,261 were already carrying rings.

We went to the Þjòrsàrver in 1951 to learn how to catch pinkfeet; and seem to have done so."

In the autumn of 1952, we recaptured six more of our old Icelandic friends. "We haven't seen you," we said to those ringed as goslings, "since you were so high."

Already we had news of no less than 187 of our Iceland-ringed geese—nearly all of them killed, and all but two recovered in Britain.

So much for the initial results of the goose-marking project which was the main object of our expedition. But the discovery of this great new breeding ground of pinkfeet was, in itself, an important result, and, in taking stock, it is interesting to discover what was previously known of the pinkfoot in Iceland. For the sake of thoroughness, and because the Iceland goose-story has been so full of muddles, we go back in history to the time of the great pioneer ornithologist of Iceland, Friedrich Faber. Faber studied Iceland's birds intensively, and widely, between 1819 and 1821; he identified two geese, one the whitefront, which he supposed to breed in northern Iceland. His other goose, which he identified as the bean-goose, but which was undoubtedly the grey lag, he stated to breed in the south only. Such was the influence of this most excellent and accurate of ornithologists that whitefronts were for more than a century believed to nest in Iceland, and many eggs were exported from that island, to find their way as genuine white-fronts' eggs into the collections of the principal European, and some American, oologists and museums. In fact, as we shall see, Faber was in this case quite wrong, and there is no evidence whatever, of any kind, that either a whitefront or a bean-goose has ever laid an egg in Iceland, though many Greenland whitefronts pass through Iceland on migration. Further, since Faber used *Anser segetum*, a name then used to describe the bean-goose, for what we now know were grey lags, many clutches of grey lags' eggs from Iceland were sent by farmers and dealers to European collections as bean-goose eggs; and even Bernhard Hantzsch, another great pioneer ornithologist who worked in Iceland in 1903, went so far as to

13. *Goslings held by Valli are ringed by Peter.* (P.T.-P.)

14. *A well-grown Whooper cygnet.* (P.T.-P.)

record the bean-goose as a " not uncommon breeding-species." And *this* was not true; there is but one real record of a bean-goose on the Iceland list. The real truth, which is that the only breeding wild geese of Iceland are grey lags round the coast and pinkfeet in the interior, took a long time to emerge,[1] and was not proved until 1929. William Proctor, the egg-agent, who was collecting in Iceland in the eighteen-thirties for several British oologists, produced what he alleged to be pinkfoot eggs, but there is no proof that his identification was correct (and he also produced alleged bean-goose eggs which were certainly those of grey lags). In August 1894 some geese shot in the flightless stage of summer moult at Þingey, about fifteen miles from the mouth of the river Skjálfandafljót in northern Iceland, were seen by the British ornithologist H. H. Slater, and these were pinkfeet. This was not formal proof that they had bred somewhere in Iceland, but made it appear likely.

* * * *

The courses of the two great rivers, the Skjálfandafljót in the north and the Þjórsá in the south, form a natural route for travellers across central Iceland. The pass runs between the ice-caps Hofsjökull and Vatnajökull, and in almost exactly the topographical centre of the island involves the crossing of a sandy desert called the Sprengisandur (Bursting Sand) which lies between the main sources of the two rivers. It takes laden ponies about twelve hours to cross the Sprengisandur, twelve hours without food, though there is plenty of water. The route, which is undoubtedly the swiftest across Iceland, was discovered by the farmer of Íshóll in 1810. Íshóll was the highest farm up the valley of the Skjálfandafljót. It is now a deserted ruin; and perhaps we should say rediscovered, for there is plenty of evidence that the farmers of the Heroic Age of the Icelandic Sagas thought nothing of crossing the interior,

[1] It occurred, however, to Alfred Newton (1863, 1864) after his visit to Iceland in 1858. Though he did not encounter breeding geese himself, he made a typically cautious, and typically correct guess.

and some evidence that they used the Þjórsá route. The first British traveller to cross was W. L. Watts in August 1875.

Watts started with a horse-train in the north at the famous duck-lake of Mývatn, crossed over to the valley of the Skjálfandafljót, left Íshóll on 21 August, made the crossing of the Sprengisandur desert on 22 August and reached that night the oasis under Arnarfell, at the north end of the oases of our 1951 expedition. Watts commented most particularly on this oasis, in which he camped, and notes that on his arrival he "disturbed a bevy of swans, which at this season of the year lose the feathers of their wings, of course, preventing their flight. Taking advantage of this [he writes], chase was immediately given, and four of the number very soon captured." Next day Watts crossed the many glacier-streams and rivers flowing from the Hofsjökull ice-cap to the Þjórsá, travelled over ground "in most places covered with swampy moss," halted at the site of our base-camp, the good grazing-ground Bólstaður, and then made his way rapidly down the Þjórsá to the farms in the south, which he reached late the next day, travelling light.

In the next year another Englishman, C. le Neve Foster, made exactly the same journey south across the Sprengisandur from Íshóll. He reached the oasis under Arnarfell earlier, on the evening of 4 August 1876. Just the same thing happened. "On reaching the hill," he writes, "we caught sight of some swans and cygnets, and tired as we were, the instincts of the chase were too strong, so we rode up the hill-side as far as we could, and then dismounting, ran after the cygnets and knocked over one or two with our riding-whips, and made a meal off them later on." Next day they rode along the edge of the terminal moraine of the south-eastern tongue of Hofsjökull, crossed the glacier rivers, and killed another swan with a riding-whip. "Of course, if the bird had been in full feather, he easily could have escaped us, but as he was moulting he could not fly far. However he could get over the ground at a very good pace."

" We then," goes on Foster, " rode along the alluvial plain formed by the tributaries which go to swell the *Þjórsá*, seeing various lakes and ponds, and plenty of swans and wild geese." This casual statement is the first indication of the whereabouts of what is perhaps the world's greatest breeding-ground of the pinkfoot, as it now appears that it may be.

Foster was probably not equipped to identify the geese that he saw, and certainly seems to have made no attempt to do so. And by quoting his encounter with geese in the upper reaches of the Þjórsá we are in danger of confusing the turn of events. For it was in the northward flowing rivers of Iceland that the pinkfoot puzzle was eventually solved, and it was up the river Skjálfandafljót and the big river Jökulsá á Fjöllum to the east of it, which drains North Vatnajökull through the vast lava-desert of Odáðahraun that the keys were found. In search of the answer the British travellers Shepherd in 1862 and Coburn in 1899 worked up the Skjálfandafljót as far as the famous waterfall Goðafoss (so called because in the year 1,000 when the Iceland Þíng formally accepted Christianity, the local farmer threw therein his household idols or gods) ; they found a great many grey lags but no other geese. They had not penetrated far enough up the river. But Shepherd was told by local farmers that " large flocks " of geese bred yet farther up the river, near its source.

It would be confusing and somewhat irrelevant to render a full account of all the naturalists who visited Iceland between 1820 (Faber) and 1929 (Congreve and Freme), together with the information which they got by their own observations (scanty), the purchase of specimens of skins and eggs from local farmers, and the questioning of the natives. It seems quite clear that as early as 1821, when F. A. L. Thienemann visited Iceland, there was already a trickle of goose eggs from the interior brought down by sheep farmers, specially for collectors. Thienemann, for instance, got six or eight eggs of what he believed to be the bean-goose.

Ever since the interior of Iceland became once more familiar to the Icelanders in the nineteenth century, eggs taken in it have been sent to collectors in Europe, though without any authentication of the species from which they were taken. A great many of them, as Congreve and Freme have shown, are in various European collections labelled whitefront. Thus in 1925 the Japanese ornithologist Hachisuka obtained five clutches from the farmer William Pálsson, which were supposed to be those of whitefronts; Pálsson told him that they bred "in Grafarlondsá and Lindáa" [*sic*]. One of these rivers is a tributary, the other a branch of the Jökulsá á Fjöllum, and there is evidence that they had been known to the farmers of the north as a great breeding place for geese for many years and certainly since the turn of the century.

It is but a sample of the astonishing muddle into which Iceland's grey geese had snared human observers that a farmer interviewed through an interpreter by Freme, who had been to Grafarlönd twenty-seven times, appeared to Freme to refer to the local breeding geese, which (when the man first knew them) existed in a very large colony, as whitefronts. We must immediately note that it is Freme who may have been confused and that all the evidence is that this colony was the remains of a pinkfoot colony. The Grafarlönd colony, then, is the first colony of Iceland's interior geese whose exact location became known to the external world, even if it was as belonging to the wrong kind of goose.

The first formal identification of the interior geese, the *heiðargæs* of the Icelanders, was made on the Skjálfandafljót on 4 June 1929. The English ornithologists W. Maitland Congreve and the late S. W. P. Freme were guided by an Iceland farmer to the place where that river is entered by a tributary, the Krossá, which flows through a deepish gorge. On the terraces of this gorge they found twenty nests, on most of which pinkfeet were incubating eggs, though some had been recently robbed —probably by foxes.

In 1931, 1932 and 1933 the late Magnús Björnsson made several late summer journeys into the interior in search of pinkfeet, visiting the headwaters of four main rivers of the north and the Þjórsá of the south. It is most convenient to discuss the results of his and other investigations under each river, starting with the:—

Skjálfandafljót

The lowest place on this river where pinkfeet may breed (though here not provedly) is at Aldeyjarfoss, where Björnsson saw them in 1932; in that year he also saw them up the Svartá tributary and at Hrafnabjörg, where the Ridley brothers found a nest in 1952. He also found colonies at the Krossá confluence (the place of the 1929 discovery) in 1932 (as did David Haig-Thomas in 1933 and Finnur Guðmundsson in 1945). The pinkfoot also breeds in Kiðagil (Guðmundsson in 1945); perhaps at Hraunárgljúfur and Langadrag on an upper tributary of the Hrauná (Björnsson in 1932); farther up the main stream in Ytra-Fljótsgil (G. in 1945); and in Syðra-Fljótsgil (B. in 1933, G. in 1945), particularly the oasis Stóraflæða. In 1945 Guðmundsson found that the main breeding-stations in the whole Skjálfandafljót river-system were in the ghylls Krossárgil (near the Krossá confluence), Kiðagil, Ytra-Fljótsgil and Syðra-Fljótsgil, and he notes that at none of the other nine breeding-places encountered either by Björnsson or himself did the number of occupied nests exceed ten. He came to the conclusion that in 1945 there were most likely not more than 200 nests in the system.

Laxá

In 1932 Björnsson found small groups which he described as pinkfeet at the Krákárbotnar and some other places along the river Kráká, which flows into the Laxá at the place where that river leaves the great duck-lake Mývatn. Timmermann, however, to whom Björnsson told his experiences soon after they had occurred, states that no pinkfeet were observed on this occasion (early August) but that Björnsson found breeding-places of the grey lag only in the Kráká headwaters. He adds: "Here, for the first time, nine young geese were ringed." Fortunately one of these was recovered; it was recorded by Witherby and Leach (1933) as ring Reykjavík 2.76, ringed Ódáðahraun 2 August 1932, recovered Inverness 22 Nov. 1932; and it had certainly been placed on a grey lag!

In 1945 Guðmundsson investigated the Kráká area thoroughly and found no geese breeding there, neither grey lags nor pinkfeet. Björnsson states, in another part of his paper, that grey lag and pinkfoot "overlap . . . both on the Svartá and the Kráká, south from Mývatn." The Svartá here referred to is a tributary of the Skjálfandafljót whose head-waters are very close to those of the Kráká.

Jökulsá á Fjöllum

Shepherd was told in 1862 that large flocks of geese bred near the source of this river, and, as we have seen, the Grafarlönd and Lindaá area has been known as a grey goose breeding-place since the turn of the century or before. As long ago as 1924, according to an informant of Freme, the colony here was "much reduced in numbers," presumably by egging. Nevertheless there were enough for Pálsson to provide Hachisuka with five "whitefront" clutches in 1925. In 1932 Brian Roberts stated that the geese had been "suffering seriously from human interference during the last ten years and had gradually decreased in number until now there are so few [in the Grafarlönd area] that it is not worth making the journey for the annual egg raid." Roberts and Peter Falk, however, thought that there was a colony in the oasis Herðubreiðarlindir, where eggs had been previously taken. The lowest nests (two) were seen by E. G. Bird and David Haig-Thomas in 1933 at the confluence of the Grafarlandaá and the Jökulsá; but these observers found no pinkfeet in the

Grafarlönd oasis itself in that year (where they camped as early as 26-28 May) nor any on the banks of the Lindaá (the lower of the two Jökulsá tributaries of that name) or in Herðubreiðarlindir. Bird and Haig-Thomas saw a few pairs in flight between the Grafarlandaá and the Lindaá; and much later in the same summer Björnssón saw some at Arnardalur, not far away.

Much farther up the Jökulsá á Fjöllum the Danish explorer J. P. Koch found on 17 June 1912 that two pairs of " graagæs "—which must have been pinkfeet—had built nests at Svartárbottnar, where the river Svartá comes out from under a sandbank 8 metres thick. By this small tributary of the Jökulsá, south-west of the hill Vaðalda, is a small oasis of *Archangelica* and grass in the desert. Koch then crossed the Jökulsá and not far from the source of its tributary the (upper) Lindaá, in an oasis known as Hvannalindir found " geese breed along the riversides " on *c.* 18 June, though he did not identify them. Roberts and Falk, however, could find no recent traces of geese in Hvannalindir between 17 and 20 July 1932. Björnsson had more success in 1933: in Hvannalindir on 2 August he shot a flightless goose and gander and two goslings, and he saw pinkfeet also in the neighbouring oases of Fagridalur and Grágæsadalur (grey goose valley). In 1948 Philip Beckett tells us that he also found breeding pinkfeet in Hvannalindir.

Jökulsá á Brú

In his exploration of 1933, Björnsson found pinkfeet in the tongue of land between this river and its tributary the Kringilsá, and found nests (probably empty) on the upper moraine of the glacier Brúarjökull, part of north-east Vatnajökull.

Þjórsá

In 1931 Magnús Björnsson tried to visit the upper reaches of the river Þjórsá in order to see the breeding-grounds which he presumed to exist there by the information of farmers and from judicious study of the distribution and position of vegetation oases. Unfortunately his attempt between 17 June and 3 July was dogged by bad weather, and though he saw fairly large flocks of pinkfeet, he could not get very far up the river before he was compelled to cut his trip short and return downstream. However, he did find one breeding ground of pinkfeet at Gljúfurleit on the middle reaches of the Þjórsá (where we found three nests on the cliffs of the basalt gorge on 24 June 1951). Next year Magnús started his journey to the Þjórsá headwaters not up-river but across country from the west, from Hvítárvatn, the lake on the east side of the ice-cap Langjökull. He soon reached the headwaters of the river Kisa, which drains the Kerlingarfjöll, the "old women's mountains," cutting down from these basalt peaks in deep gorges. On these gorges, the Kisubotnar, were pinkfoot colonies, he was told. When he had entered the Þjórsárver oases he discovered deserted goose-nests at the end of July "to the south-east of the [Hofsjökull] glacier," and encountered pinkfeet. This was just the place at which Foster had seen "plenty of wild geese" in 1876. And across the Þjórsá from here, in the neighbouring oasis Eyvindarkofaver, Magnús met fairly large pinkfoot flocks on 27 and 28 July, including nearly flying young. But he did not find any empty nests.

In 1950 the Icelandic geologist Guðmundur Kjartansson visited the terminal moraine of the Hofsjökull glacier, Arnarfellsmúlar. He estimated that there were about a hundred on the whole circuit of this deserted, overgrown moraine, from which the glacier has retreated over half a mile in the last fifty years, Guðmundur told Finnur Guðmundsson. This finally confirmed Finnur's view that a large unaccounted-for pinkfoot breeding-population was harboured by this largest central oasis of Iceland, the Þjórsárver. Finnur's view was also strengthened by his conversations with the farmers of the Þjórsárdalur who come up to the river's source in late summer

15*a*. *A camp below the terminal moraine of the Hofsjökull on which many geese breed.* (F.G.)

b. *Lush vegetation on the terminal moraine, mostly* Sedum roseum (*Midsummer men*). (F.G.)

16. *Jökulkriki from Ólafsfell—the birth of the glacier tributaries of the Þjórsá.* (P.T.-P.)

and autumn to collect their sheep and hunt foxes. These farmers had seen many *heiðargæs* in the Þjórsárver við Hofsjökul.

That these farmers had, indeed, seen some members of what might then have been described as the "great missing population" of the pinkfoot is now clear. Up to now we have refrained from any sort of estimate of the actual population that we encountered in the Þjórsárver við Hofsjökul in 1951. But as is described in some detail in Appendix E (p. 219) we made many efforts to measure the breeding-population of these oases, by two main methods: the counting of nests in sample measured areas; and the study of the number of marked birds recaptured in subsequent catches. We came to the conclusion that in our year there were likely to have been approximately 2,300 nests; 5,500 adults, including non-breeders; and 7,500 goslings. There seemed to be some evidence that 1951 was a "good" year for breeding and the output of young.

This population amounts (again, approximately) to about a third of the world population; and to at least three-quarters of the Icelandic population.

At least two of those who took part in the wild-goose chase up the Þjórsá think that the pinkfoot is the most romantic bird in the world. The other two often think they may be right. Let us hope its lonely and lovely headquarters under the white icecap remain its sanctuary for ever, the nursery of many another THOUSAND GEESE.

APPENDIX A

THE PINKFOOT IN SPITSBERGEN

THE FIRST EGGS of this species known to science were taken by the British explorers Edward Evans and Wilson Sturge on 27 June 1855 from nests of geese (which, such was the confusion in those times, they thought were grey lags) which they found on the shore of Coal Bay (Colesbukta), which lies on the south side of the great Ice Fjord (Isfjorden) that nearly cuts the high Arctic island of Spitsbergen in half. That the breeding grey geese of Spitsbergen were, in fact, pinkfeet was determined by the great British ornithologist Alfred Newton and the Swedish ornithologist A. J. Malmgren, as together they handled fresh specimens on a schooner at anchor in Safe Haven (Trygghamna) in Ice Fjord, in July 1864. The many subsequent expeditions to Spitsbergen have shown the pinkfoot to be a widespread nester on the raised beaches and up the valleys of that archipelago, nesting on mounds on the tundra, and on little cliffs and buttresses of the steep eroded mountains of that Arctic land, never in great colonies or dense groups. In August in Spitsbergen Fisher has seen several flocks of under a hundred, each formed probably by the dozen or so families reared in one wide valley.

The western part of the complex archipelago of Svalbard, as it is now usually called, is composed of a high plateau much dissected by weather and frost into a maze of valleys. Over parts of this plateau are large ice-caps from which glacier tongues creep into many of the valleys. The retreat of the ice since the end of the Ice Age has left most of the valleys broadened into U-section by ice action, full of alluvium brought down from the melt rivers that run in summer from the glaciers. There are wide expanses of lakes, bogs and vegetation-covered tundra between the mountains near the sea. Further, the relaxation of the weight of ice on Spitsbergen has evidently allowed the country to rise in stages some feet from the sea, and raised beaches in tiers can be detected round nearly all the Spitsbergen coast. A typical Spitsbergen landscape consists of steep-topped, much-gullied mountains of very much the same height as each other, with steep slopes of talus below their cliffs formed by the weathering of the precipices, running down to a flat plain, often a mile wide, which lies between them and the sea. This last is formed by a raised beach and is only occasionally traversed by water-courses which cut down the final twenty or thirty feet to sea-level. It is on these raised beaches that the pinkfeet of Spitsbergen feed, and they usually nest on the steep sides of the water-course gullies on ledges of cliffs where the foxes cannot get at them.

A study of the literature of the pinkfoot in Spitsbergen shows that small colonies breed in most years in all the sheltered valleys of west Spitsbergen, especially those communicating with the big fiords that cut right into it from the west. A few pinkfeet also nest on Edge Island (Edgeöya) on the south-east side of West Spitsbergen. It is perhaps worth making a short tour of the pinkfoot grounds of Spitsbergen to develop this picture, which owes much to British explorers of the last century, and in particular to expeditions sponsored by and largely composed of members of the University of Oxford; and to the recent (unpublished) investigations of the Norwegian ornithologist, Herman L. Løvenskiöld, which he has most kindly and freely allowed us to use.

Starting in the south of the main island, West (Vest) Spitsbergen, we find a breeding-place quite near the south cape, on the west coast of Sörkapp Land between Stormbukta and Suffolkpynten. Here on the broad coastal plain with its island-dotted lake Løvenskiöld found a flock of 25 on 14 July 1950, quite flightless: five or six pairs had small goslings. Two days later his party found twenty-seven pinkfeet, of which only three could fly, scattered over the plain.

The most important inlet in the south of West Spitsbergen is Horn Sound (Hornsund), and on the south side of this fiord an anchorage known as Goose Bay or Gåshamna was found by Bianchi's Russian expedition of 1899 and 1900 to be a breeding-place of pinkfeet. In 1899 the geese were going south on 12 and 13 September, and in 1900 their flocks arrived on 13 May. A flock was present on 7 September 1882 in Horn Sound when the English voyager Cocks visited that place. On the north side, under Rotges Mount (a great breeding-place of little auks), the explorer von Heuglin found the pinkfoot abundant and breeding, with young, on 16 July 1870, and near here by the lake Revevatnet in the narrow valley Revedalen Løvenskiöld saw four families—twenty-five geese in all—on 4 August 1950. Later in the same day his party met with thirty grown geese at Hyttevikken, on the mainland north of the entrance to Horn Sound opposite the Dun Islands (Dunöyane).

In the great inlet Bell Sound (Bellsund), north of Horn Sound, the pinkfoot breeds in the valleys of Recherchefjorden and van Keulenfjorden, on Axel Island (Akselöya) which bars the mouth of van Mijenfjorden, and in van Mijenfjorden itself. In Recherchefjorden Cocks saw a great flock on 22 September 1882, but the pinkfoot was not proved to breed in this branch of Bell Sound until the Swedish naturalist Gustav Kolthoff found it so in 1898. On the west side of Recherchefjorden Løvenskiöld disturbed a flying flock of twelve birds, of which six were adults, on 18 August 1948; and in 1950 the geologist Winsnes told him that a great number nested on Observationfjellet farther east.

On 10 July 1864 A. J. Malmgren shot a pinkfoot goose on her nest on Middle Hook (Midterhuken), the promontory that divides van Mijenfjorden from van Keulenfjorden, and gave two of the eggs upon which it was sitting to Alfred Newton. A. G. Nathorst's account of his visit to van Mijenfjorden with Kolthoff in early July 1898 suggests that the pinkfeet probably occupied much of the tundra from Middle Hook eastwards along the south side of that long inlet. In 1881 Cocks saw some adult pinkfeet up Van Keulenfjorden on 1 August. In 1898 the species was seen breeding there by two separate expeditions, and Koenig's big ornithological expeditions of 1907 and 1908 found it breeding abundantly.

In 1881, on 31 July, Cocks found pinkfeet on a low-lying and mossy corner of Axel Island all among old ribs and bones of right whales of Spitsbergen's whaling days; and Kolthoff confirmed this as a breeding-place in 1898; he also saw large moulting flocks on the low capes in van Mijenfjorden on 7 July.

There is yet another breeding-station in Bell Sound, for at Kapp Martin, the north portal of its entrance, Løvenskiöld found a flying party of two adults and five young on 28 August 1948. Between 5 and 15 August 1949 Løvenskiöld and his assistant found flocks of from six to thirty-nine geese between Kapp Martin and Lowe Ness (Lågneset).

The greatest of all the Spitsbergen fiords is Ice Fjord, which runs more than a hundred miles into its hinterland from its middle west. Pinkfeet breed in all the valleys round this great fiord, from Kapp Linné and Kapp Staratschin (Festningen) on the south side of its entrance to Safe Haven (Trygghamna) on the north side.

It was at Cape Staratschin that the British ornithologist Aubyn Trevor-Battye found a pair on 18 June 1896; and on the lake Linnévatnet between it and Kapp Linné Løvenskiöld saw a pinkfoot goose with five half-grown goslings on 22 August 1948—none could fly.

At Green Harbour (Grönfjorden), east of Cape Staratschin, Cocks saw a pair in 1881; on 4 July 1894 the English naturalist-explorer H. W. Feilden disturbed what was probably a family party here. And the Germans Römer and Schaudinn found birds with young on 16 July 1898. O. von Zedlitz found them breeding at Green Harbour in 1910, and the Dutch naturalist G. J. van Oordt found them very common there at the beginning of September 1921. However, since then the Russian coal-mining concession in the valley has been developed. Fisher saw no pinkfeet there on the Oxford expedition of 1933: they are not tolerant of the presence of man.

It was in Coal Bay (Colesbukta), to the east of Green Harbour, that Evans and Sturge took the first known clutch of pinkfoot eggs on 27 June 1855. C. J. Sundevall found the pinkfoot breeding here in August 1868, as did Kolthoff in 1900 and Koenig in 1908. As in Coal Bay, in Advent Bay (Adventfjorden) there is quite a colony, though it has retreated up valley with the development of the Norwegian coal-mining settlement. Alfred Newton came to possess an egg which A. J. Malmgren took there on 4 July 1864. On 20 June 1896 Trevor-Battye saw flocks of twenty-two and fourteen flying up to the head of Advent Bay. The big flock in Advent Bay on 23 September 1898 may have been on passage, but the birds seen there on 19 May 1899, the first of the season, may well have been going to breed, and certainly pinkfeet were breeding in the long east-running Advent Valley (Adventdalen) when Koenig visited it on 15 June 1908, and have been found breeding there, in the same area as the much rarer barnacle-goose, by all ornithologists since. Moreover, at least a few remain in the coastal area of Advent Bay, for Løvenskiöld saw six near Longyearbyen on the south side on 3 July 1950. Advent Valley communicates by an inland pass with a side valley of the broad Sassendalen, up which Martin Conway made his first crossing of Spitsbergen in 1896. Since Cocks saw a flock there on 14 September 1882 Sassendalen was suspected of being very suitable for pinkfeet. On 3 July 1896 Conway and his companions camped where the Esker valley cuts down into Sassendalen through a limestone gorge. Just at this place, by a waterfall, was a colony of pinkfeet occupying a dozen nests. Unfortunately the geese were so much disturbed by the campers that glaucous gulls ate all their eggs and fledglings on 5 July. In 1899, on the north side of Sassendalen, the English naturalist H. N. Bonar found three empty pinkfoot nests on 28 July " on a narrow tongue of rock with precipitous sides, formed at the junction of two torrents, about nine miles inland among the Colorado Hills." The site was a very typical one—on an inaccessible, grass-covered ledge. Koenig in 1907 and 1908 and all subsequent expeditions have found nests in the gorges round the edge of Sassendalen. On 16 August 1950 Løvenskiöld disturbed a big flock of pinkfeet on the largest lake in Sassendalen. They swam to the shore and disappeared in the bogs. At the same lake there were fifty-three geese on both 19 and 23 August; and he saw a great number more at the river-delta on 19 August, and three flocks amounting to over a hundred birds in all (quite separate from the flock of fifty-three) flew over on 23 August.

The south entrance to Sassen Bay (Sassenfjorden) is guarded by the bastion Diabasodden, and here Løvenskiöld found twenty-three pinkfeet on 24 August 1950, some of which were young and not able to fly as well as their parents.

On the north side of Sassen Bay the Gips Valley (Gipsdalen) comes down between Mount Temple and Gips Hook. Here Seton Gordon found a pinkfoot nest in a patch of *Dryas octopetala* and *Saxifraga oppositifolia*, with the remains of seven nests of previous years, evidence that this was an intensely traditional site. Some miles up the valley other geese could be seen passing to and fro from their feeding grounds. In 1933 Fisher, with C. H. Hartley, walked to Gips Valley from Bruce City, farther north, and saw several family parties of flightless pinkfeet in July. On 17 August 1950 Løvenskiöld was in Gips Valley when nine pinkfeet flew over him, and later in the day he encountered forty geese, adults and young, only nine of which could fly, under Mount Temple (Templefjellet).

Round Bruce City the Scottish Spitsbergen Syndicate Hut on the wide raised beach on the east side of Klaas Billen Bay no pinkfeet were provedly breeding in 1933, though our expedition encountered a flightless party of twenty on 10 July. But on 15 July 1921 van Oordt found a nest with three eggs and a newly hatched young one at Bruce City. Later, on 19 July, Seton Gordon found a number of pinkfoot nests close to where the Nordenskiöld glacier flows into Klaas Billen Bay (Billefjorden). In 1921, too, the same observer found, on 14 July, pinkfeet just going into moult but still able to fly, in the upper reaches of Ebba Valley, at the very head of Klaas Billen Bay. In the Mimer Valley opposite, Gordon and van Oordt found pinkfeet in full moult on 15 July.

Mimer Bay is on the east side of the promontory Dicksonland, which runs south between the two main arms of the ice fiord. It ends in Kapp Thordson, where several pinkfeet were seen on 12 September 1882 by Cocks, and a young one was shot. From the western arm of Ice Fjord, known as North Fjord (Nordfjorden), runs an indentation, Ekman Bay (Ekmanfjorden), where Trevor-Battye found two broods on 24 June 1896. In 1921 van Oordt and his colleague Einar Wirén found several nests of pinkfeet on the top of a mountain (Mount Lundbohm) here, and many on the top of precipitous cliffs, in river gorges, and near the edge of the steep coast. On Coraholmen, the big island in Ekman Bay, Løvenskiöld found twenty-eight geese with a great number of goslings on 21 July 1948. Here, in August 1950, as Løvenskiöld was told, a man from Longyearbyen, the Norwegian settlement in Advent Bay, shot ninety geese, thus probably exterminating the entire population of the island.

At Cape Boheman (Bohemanneset), the south-west portal of North Fjord, Trevor-Battye obtained the female pinkfoot with its nest, eggs and some turf, now in the British Museum, on a small island on 26 June 1896. Kolthoff saw big flocks here on 19 July 1898, and van Oordt several small troops in June and July 1921. Kolthoff found two nests; van Oordt did not find any near Cape Boheman. Finally, the redoubtable Alfred Newton found the pinkfoot breeding (one nest) at Safe Haven on 16 July 1864.

We can now proceed to enumerate the many pinkfoot grounds beyond Ice Fjord. W. S. Bruce, the great Scottish explorer of Spitsbergen, found the pinkfoot breeding on the northern part of the west coast of Prince Charles Foreland (Prins Karls Forland) on 18 July 1906, when he secured a gosling and came across several gaggles on 18 July. On 20 July he also records pinkfeet at the north promontory of Prince Charles Foreland, the great seabird rock of Vogel Hook (Fuglehuken), where Will. Barents made his landfall when he discovered Spitsbergen in 1596. The Koenig expedition of 1907 found pinkfeet breeding in both southern and northern parts of the west coast of Prince Charles Foreland. In 1921 Seton Gordon found two nests at Vogel Hook on 29 June, and took an excellent photograph of one of them on the precipitous face.

On the west coast of the mainland the pinkfeet were breeding abundantly at King's Bay (Kongsfjorden) in June 1898 (Römer and Schaudinn) and the Koenig expeditions of 1907 and 1908 found nests on some of the islands in the bay. In 1900 pinkfeet were on the Lovén Islands here, Count Zedlitz records, but he did not see any on these in 1910. C. T. Dalgety found two nests in King's Bay in 1930. From the settlement Ny Alesund in King's Bay Løvenskiöld learned of breeding in 1948, and in 1949 he found two nests on the island Gordöya on 28 June and saw a single pinkfoot flying round another island Storholmen; later, on 2 August, he saw a flock of twelve geese in this island group.

Zedlitz recorded a breeding-place in 1910 at Möllerfjorden on the east side of Cross Bay (Krossfjorden), the great inlet that shares a mouth with King's Bay, but runs northerly. Among the magnificent scenery of Magdalena Bay (Magdalenefjord) in the north-west, A. H. Cocks and Abel Chapman saw three pairs of pinkfeet flying about under the local Rotges Mount or little auk breeding ground. On searching, they caught half a dozen young ones running about on the snow. In the north-westernmost corner of Spitsbergen, at Smeerenberg Bay (Smeerenburgfjorden), the haunt of the old right whalers, pinkfeet were seen in some numbers by Arnold Pike in August and September of 1888. In this fjord, on the eastern lagoon of Amsterdam Island (Amsterdamöya) Løvenskiöld saw fourteen pinkfeet on 2 July 1949, and three flying over Bear Haven (Björnhamna) in South Gat (Sörgattet) on 4 July.

The most northerly breeding ground of the pinkfoot in Spitsbergen, and indeed in the world, appears to be the peninsulas north of Liefde Bay (Liefdefjorden), in the northern part of West Spitsbergen. In 1949 at the mountain Rabotfjellet in the south of the peninsula Biskayerhuken Løvenskiöld found a pair with new-hatched young and another with hatching eggs on 12 July. The larger Reindeer Peninsula (Reinsdyrflya) was found to be a pinkfoot breeding ground by the Oxford expedition of 1921, or at least presumed so, for moulted primaries were picked up on 7 July and birds shot on 17 July were incapable of flight (F. C. R. Jourdain). In 1923 T. G. Longstaff found a flightless flock in moult, on the south side of the Peninsula "deep in Liefde Bay." In 1949 Løvenskiöld saw, at Worsleyneset in Liefde Bay, five flying and sixteen flightless pinkfeet on 21 July. On the same day he saw six adults and a pair with three small goslings on the near-by Station Islands (Andöyane), and on 25 July twelve pinkfeet on the southernmost of these islands. At a mountain, Schleyfjell, near the head of Liefde Bay he saw a pair with three small goslings on 21 July.

In 1924 another Oxford expedition had rather dramatic proof

of birds in this north part of West Spitsbergen, when at Cape Roos (Roosneset) on the south side of Liefde Bay they observed " a combat between a pink-footed goose and an arctic fox. The fight was taking place on the shore of the bay and the goose was holding its own comfortably. Being disturbed on the approach of a boat, the bird retreated; the next minute the fox ran off, bearing an egg in its mouth. There's little doubt that he would have failed in his attack but for our intervention." On 27 July 1949 Løvenskiöld found a biggish flock at Cape Roos—about twelve adults with a large number (probably over twenty-four) of young in different stages.

In 1930 Dalgety saw a few birds in Liefde Bay, but found no nests; this part of Spitsbergen has quite a lot of vegetation in the summer, but it is clear that the pinkfoot population is not very large. There is, however, one more probable breeding-place in the neighbourhood of Liefde Bay—on Kapp Kjeldsen, which is the east bastion of Bock Bay (Bockfjorden), Løvenskiöld found twelve adult geese on 27 July 1949.

In the rest of Svalbard there are but two more known breeding-grounds. Nowhere in the north-eastern two-thirds of the archipelago has it been proved to breed, though individual birds and sometimes small flocks have been seen by various expeditions in Hinlopen Strait and on Barents Island. In the remote Wyches Islands (Kong Karls Land) south-east of North-East Land (Nordaustlandet) Gustav Kolthoff in 1898 found droppings, egg-shells and empty nests on Kongsöya, which he believed to be those of pinkfeet, and lists an " *Anser* sp. (prob. *brachyrhynchus*) " as " certainly breeding " (A. G. Nathorst, 1899). In the same year, on 4 August, Römer and Schaudinn saw several individuals on Swedish Foreland (Svensköya).

On Edge Island there is a pinkfoot ground in the vegetation-covered valley that runs inland north from Keilhau Bay on the west side of Deevie Bay (Tjuvfjorden). Between 1743 and 1749 four Russian sailors were accidentally left on shore on Edge Island, on which they lived for six years and three months, three surviving. Their ship was never heard of again, so nobody knew they were stranded, and they were only rescued by chance. The story of their survival is a remarkable one, and they recorded that, among the other desirable food animals, geese, ducks and other waterfowl were seen in summer. It is quite likely that they may have owed their lives partly to pinkfeet. The German explorer A. Walter saw small flocks here at the end of May 1899, and in early August

1927 C. T. Dalgety found a small flock of pinkfeet accompanied by two or three broods of young, at Keilhau Bay.

A trapper who wintered on the east side of Deevie Bay, near Ziegler Island (Ziegleröya) told Løvenskiöld that he saw a flock of fifty pinkfeet on 8 September 1950, ten birds on 29 May, four on 3 June, and two on 10 July 1951.

To sum up, then, the pinkfoot breeds in Svalbard on one place on the west of Sörkapp Land, at least two grounds in Horn Sound, at least five in Bell Sound, about fifteen in the valleys and raised beaches in Ice Fjord, in three or more places on Prince Charles Foreland, in King's Bay, Magdalena Bay, and Smeerenberg Bay, and on at least four grounds in the Leifde Bay—Reindeer Peninsula region. It is known to breed nowhere else in Svalbard except in small numbers on Kong Karls Land and Edge Island. Nowhere do any of the accounts suggest the existence of semi-colonies of more than a dozen or twenty nests, and when observers write of a large flock in Spitsbergen they seldom mean a hundred birds. Neither of us would be surprised if it were proved that the average annual number of nests occupied in Spitsbergen was well under a thousand. The pinkfeet always appear to breed within easy reach of suitable valley tundra grazing grounds, but when they do not breed on small islands, where they may occupy flat ground, they almost invariably nest on ledges, on cliffs and the walls of gorges. No doubt this is an adaptation to counter the predation of the arctic fox, though gander and goose together are said to be able to drive a fox away from a nest.

APPENDIX B

THE PINKFOOT IN GREENLAND

IN THE SUMMER of 1823 Captain Douglas Charles Clavering, F.R.S., the young Commander of H.M.S. *Griper*, forced his ship to, and discovered a large part of the topography of, a substantial stretch of the coast of North-East Greenland. The object of his voyage was to take Captain Sabine of the Royal Artillery as far north as possible on the eastern coast of Greenland in order to make observations on the pendulum. On 14 August he landed Sabine on Pendulum Island, not far south of latitude 75° N., and while the soldier was engaged in his observations, he explored the coast to the south in ship's boats—which he continued to do until the re-embarkation of the observatory on 30 August. During this period his party became the last, and indeed probably the only, white men to see a family of the old Eskimos of North-East Greenland alive, and probably the first white men to see the Greenland pinkfoot. The Eskimos were encountered on 18 August on the south side of the large island that now bears Clavering's name; and we believe that it was pinkfeet that Clavering alluded to in the following sentence: "We shot some swans, which we found excellent eating." This was on 21 August, when Clavering was within a few miles of the head of the long inlet which he christened Loch Fyne, which separates the great peninsula Hold-with-Hope from Hudson Land.

In his excellent and scholarly *Birds of Greenland* (1950) Finn Salomonsen states, "The only (thing) one can say is that this observation must refer to some large water-birds, no doubt flightless at the time, but it sounds certainly unlikely that it should have been swans so far north; I would imagine the confusion occurred with some sort of geese." The only swans known in Greenland are stray whoopers from Iceland, where their nearest breeding-grounds are more than five hundred miles south of Loch Fyne. The whooper does not even breed in South Greenland to-day, though it probably nested there until about a hundred years ago. It is possible that the birds Clavering saw were barnacle-geese, but almost certain that they were pinkfeet, for the pinkfoot is the common big anserine of Loch Fyne to-day.

After Clavering's visit the North-East Greenlanders died out: but their occupation is marked by large numbers of their semi-underground houses, graves, tent-rings and kitchen-middens all along the coast, and most particularly along the stretch from Scoresby Sund to Hochstetters Forland, which is the main breeding-ground of the pinkfoot in Greenland. And it is in the kitchen-middens that goose-bones have been found. When C. B. Thostrup (1912) first mentions these, they were alluded to as "those of the *sædgaas*—the Danish word for bean-goose. Bean-geese and pinkfoot are con-specific, and their bones (except those of the anterior part of the head and bill) indistinguishable. The Eskimos had been eating pinkfeet.

Greenland's greatest fiord, Scoresby Sund (Sound), was discovered by the great whaling captain, scholar and explorer, W. Scoresby, junior, in 1822; it was named after his father. Scoresby and his father and some of the other whaler captains spent many days ashore in Jameson Land on the north side of the inlet, penetrating up Hurry Inlet into what we now know to be one of the headquarters of the Greenland pinkfoot. They obtained many fine specimens of plants, and the first examples known to science of the Greenland lemming. They made many observations on the birds. Unfortunately, several of the "ducks, partridges and other birds that they had shot, instead of being carefully preserved and brought on board, were, without scruple or care, coarsely skinned, broiled and eaten on the spot"—by the sailors; which, as Scoresby says, "proved an unfortunate contrivance for our zoological collection." At that time, the very end of July, the pinkfoot would have been flightless. It seems likely that if the sailors had not taken their cooking pots with them, Scoresby might have been the discoverer of the Greenland pinkfoot. In fact, the first formal identification of the species in Greenland, as we shall see, was made in 1891 in Scoresby Sund by E. Bay. It is true that on 2 August 1870 on Jackson Ø (Island), off the north-east corner of Hold-with-Hope, and not far from where Clavering saw his "swans," Dr. R. Copeland, of the German *Hansa* expedition under Captain K. Koldewey, "picked up on the shore several black feathers, which undoubtedly belonged to two different kinds of duck [*sic*], the *Anser albifrons* and *leucopsis*." They were identified as such by O. Finsch. *Leucopsis* is the barnacle goose, *albifrons* the scientific name of the whitefront, which breeds in West, not East, Greenland. It seems clear that the grey goose feather was that of a pinkfoot.

The breeding range of the pinkfoot in East Greenland as known at present runs from Mikisfjord, a shortish inlet just east of the settlement Kangerdlugssuaq, in Kong Christian IX Land north for a distance of over 600 miles at least as far as Hochstetters Forland and possibly to Mørke Fjord north of it. Until Magnus Degerbøl and U. Møhl-Hansen found it in Mikisfjord, which is in the Low Arctic region, it was thought to have a purely High Arctic distribution in Greenland, beginning where the High Arctic begins at Scoresby Sund. However, on 6 August 1932 Degerbøl and Møhl-Hansen caught a flightless gander and three well-grown goslings in Mikisfjord and in a vegetation-filled valley in the Mikisfjord hinterland saw three geese on 22 August, and many signs of grazing. Farther south the species is unknown as a breeder, though it is known on passage at Angmagssalik, particularly in September and possibly in spring, for on 31 May 1930 F. S. Chapman saw a skein of between 1,000 and 1,500 geese just west of Angmagssalik, flying north-west up a fiord, which he was almost certain were pinkfeet. As far as we can discover, the only June record is of one shot on 11 June 1901 at Angmagssalik Fjord.

The separation of the Low Arctic breeding outpost in Mikisfjord from the fertile tundras of Scoresby Sund is made complete by the barren Blosseville coast. Finn Salomonsen's excellent summary of the situation in Scoresby Sund hints that it may breed on the very little known south coast, and no doubt it is very widespread in the interior, judging from the very large number that pass to and from this region (which is also very little known to ornithologists) on migration. Indeed, the best account of the pinkfoot in the Scoresby Sund interior is still that of E. Bay, the first to identify the species in Greenland on the Ryder expedition of 1891–92. "As early as 1891," he writes, "flocks of geese were repeatedly seen in the inner part of Scoresby Sound, which were undoubtedly of this species. Such observations were made, for instance, on 18 and 27 August. The first one was shot on 5 June 1892, and from then on they were continuously seen in pairs or in flocks on Denmark Island." On 25 July, Bay shot two geese, and on 16 and 25 July flightless adults. Altogether he brought back seventy skins.

There is a largish pinkfoot population in fertile Jameson Land on the north-east side of Scoresby Sund. Much of it is concentrated around the shores of Hurry Fjord (Inlet), and there is a big colony in some years at Constable Pynt on the west side of this inlet. But the pinkfeet are also found on the south and west coasts of Jameson Land as far as Nordøst Fjord. The first certain record of the pinkfoot in Jameson Land is that of the Swedish geologist A. G. Nathorst, whose dog caught a moulting pinkfoot on 3 August 1899 where the Ryder's River runs into the north end of the fiord north-west of the Fame Islands. In the following year the " very large flock of moulting geese " in Hurry Fjord, seen by N. E. K. Hartz of the Amdrup-Hartz expedition on 10 August are very likely to have been pinkfeet.

Our knowledge of the pinkfoot in Jameson Land and Hurry Fjord has been largely contributed by Alwin Pedersen, who visited Scoresby Sund in many years from 1924 onwards. In 1925 he saw the first flocks moving into Scoresby Sund on 24 May, and pairs passed through Kap Hope, the east bastion of the entrance to Hurry Fjord in early June. He found pairs taking up territories all along the east coast of Hurry Fjord as far as the Klit Dal (Valley) through which Ryder's River flows into the north end of the fiord, The first pinkfeet of 1929 were seen by him on 23 May, and the passage was very much the same. As early as 25 May 1928 some of the geese had begun to occupy breeding ground on Constable Pynt on the west side of the fiord, and after studying this colony through June, he made a careful search for nests on 7 July 1928, discovering thirty pairs and twenty-one nests. In 1929, however, there were no nests on 10 June; it appears to have been a non-breeding year in this place. Apart from the stations at Constable Pynt and the probable breeding-ground in Klit Dal, Pedersen often observed pinkfeet in some marshes on the west coast of Jameson Land in June 1929, though he did not formally prove breeding.

In 1933 Colin Bertram, David Lack and Brian Roberts found the pinkfoot common in Hurry Fjord, but saw no broods, and at Constable Pynt on 2 August found the remains of only one nest of the season. This appears, however, to be somewhat contradicted by P. Tcherniakofsky, who estimated the number of pairs nesting in 1933 as between a hundred and fifty and two hundred.

As Salomonsen comments, the pinkfoot is not proved as a breeder in the country between Scoresby Sund and Franz Josephs Fjord, though there is some evidence that it may nest in the sheltered country at the head of Kong Oskars Fjord. E. Siggeson, of the Norwegian Greenland expedition, noticed a small flock in Segelsällskapets Fjord on 10 August 1930, a small flock in Røhss Fjord on 14 August, and a large flock at Vega Sund on 17 August.

On the same day, on Ella Ø, opposite the entrance to Vega Sund, Bernt Løppenthin found a great quantity of goose droppings and a piece of eggshell which he thought probably originated from pinkfeet.

The country north of Kaiser Franz Josephs Fjord appears to have a rather high pinkfoot population, distributed in the lands round Moskusokse Fjord, which separates Hudson Land from the Gauss Halvø (Peninsula); Mackenzie Bugt, which separates the Gauss Halvø from Hold-with-Hope; on the east coast of Hold-with-Hope; and the grounds of Loch Fyne, which separates Hold-with-Hope from Hudson Land. In Moskusokse Fjord the Swedish explorer Gustav Kolthoff found the pinkfoot in great numbers in August 1900. In 1930 Siggeson of the Norwegian Greenland expedition noted a small flock on 6 August, and on 10 August Bernt Løppenthin of the Danish Godthåb expedition found the empty nests of a pinkfoot colony among creeping willow and dwarf birch at the rim of a precipice in Parallel Valley on Gauss Halvø. On 12 August, in the fiord, they encountered a flock of 30 young and old keeping closely together, of which only a few adults could fly. In the summer of 1936 Bird and Bird obtained the head of a pinkfoot which had been shot the previous summer, outside the trapper's hut at Hoelsbu in Moskusokse Fjord.

In 1900 Kolthoff saw large flocks of pinkfeet in Mackenzie Bugt. The Norwegian expedition of 1930 reported several birds at the shore station there, Myggbukta, on 30 July, and the Bird brothers obtained three males and a female at Myggbukta between 25 May and 28 August 1937. In 1921 and 22 a few pinkfeet were collected by Danish hunters on Karlshavn, on the east side of Hold-with-Hope; and on 5 August 1930 at Knudshoved, just south of this place, Løppenthin saw a large flight of fifty or sixty birds, of which only four to six were flightless. Since Clavering's discovery of Loch Fyne in 1823 (see p. 199), it has been found to be an important breeding-place of pinkfeet by Pedersen, who found a breeding-ground on the east coast in 1932, at the mouth of a fairly large glacier stream. In the first days of August 1938 Pedersen found big flocks in Loch Fyne with half-fledged young, and he found a breeding colony of about forty nests on the west coast of the fiord.

North of Hudson Land and Hold-with-Hope lies Gael Hamkes Bugt, in which, in 1870, Koldewey's expedition found probable pinkfoot feathers on Jackson Ø. In this area on 23 July 1929 on both sides of Tyroler Fjord, from Cape May on Clavering Ø to Woolaston Forland and Kap Borlase Warren, the expedition of

Lauge Koch " everywhere along the coast encountered large flocks of geese and in the course of the day secured several. Owing to the moulting, the birds were unable to fly." In 1932 Pedersen found a single nest at Dødemans Bugt on Clavering Ø (the Deadman's Bay where Clavering saw the last of the Eskimos), and a colony on Woollaston Forland. In Young Fjord Inlet Løppenthin found " a few pinkfeet roaming about in couples on 13 and 14 July 1930 "; and near Kap Stosch he saw four birds on 3 August of the same year. North of Woollaston Forland in the coast culminating in Ardencaple Fjord and Hochstetters Forland, many pinkfeet were breeding on Kuhn Ø in 1933, according to Pedersen. In June 1930 pinkfeet often came looking for food near the station on Hochstetters Forland, and flew up Ardencaple Fjord when they had finished eating. In 1933 Pedersen found the pinkfoot breeding in Peters Bugt in the south part of Hochstetters Forland, and he pointed out that the species did not breed in Ardencaple Fjord, and that most of the birds of Hochstetters Forland were non-breeding young. These immature birds of Hochstetters Forland were particularly noted by C. G. Bird in 1938; he spent the summer at Peters Bugt and found the country " extraordinarily favourable " for pinkfeet, " which breed along the glacier streams." It is probable that the pinkfoot range extends at least to the northern part of Hochstetters Forland, though Pedersen in August 1938 was only able to find droppings there. But beyond it, there is no proof of breeding, though when Pedersen was staying in Dove Bugt in August 1933 he saw a flight of six pinkfeet coming from the interior of Mørke Fjord and making for Dove Bugt.

To sum up, the Greenland population does not appear to be large, and it seems quite possible that Chapman's big migratory flock of 1,000 to 1,500 in May near Angmagssalik may have comprised a large proportion of the total. At only one place, at Constable Pynt in Hurry Fjord, does it seem likely that there may be more than a hundred nests. And the only vegetation-oases that appear to be occupied at all densely are those of Jameson Land and the Muskusokse Fjord-Loch Fyne areas. The colonies appear to be more often in the deltas of glacier rivers than on precipices in the foothills, in this way resembling more those in central Iceland than those in Spitsbergen, or the upper reaches of the Iceland rivers. But this distinction can be overstressed, as it has been by Pedersen, and both types of nesting are often found in all the three countries in which the pinkfoot breeds.

This analysis of the distribution in Greenland, though unavoidably tedious, serves to show—indeed, to accentuate—the fact that in the truly High Arctic part of the pinkfoot's breeding range, its numbers are spread very thinly over a vast area and at the end of the season only a few families can find each other and form a flock. Only in the great central oasis of Iceland can the word thousands be legitimately used.

APPENDIX C

NOTES ON THE BIRDS OF THE ÞJÓRSÁRVER VIÐ HOFSJÖKUL

(*Reprinted from the Fifth Annual Report of the Severn Wildfowl Trust*)

[RAVEN (*Corvus corax*).—Seen in the Þjórsá valley during the return journey, about sixty miles from the oasis. It is remarkable that a bird so common in Iceland should have been so completely absent from the pinkfoot colony.]

1. SNOW-BUNTING (*Plectrophenax nivalis*).—Not uncommon breeding bird. Several pairs seen in oasis. One nest (*C*.5) found 26 June in wall of *kofi* (shepherd's hut). Hatching-date was not certain; eventually three young flew on 20 July. Nest had two entrances; male always entered and left by the same entrance, female left by this entrance but always entered by the other. On 9 July the nest was watched from a hide from 11.58 till 15.12. During the 3¼ hours the male brought food twelve times, the female seventeen times and in addition the female brooded the young for periods of 20½ mins., 5 mins. and 4½ mins. All feeds consisted of black flies except one which consisted of green sawfly larvæ (taken from *Salix glauca*). During period female was seen to emerge with fæcal sac seven times, male once. Male always sang in flight after leaving nest. Weather warm for first half, cool and rainy for second half. Parents' visits no less frequent in rain except for 20 minutes' brooding period. On 10 July the nest was watched from 13.03 to 14.49. In the 1¾ hours the male brought food ten times, the female thirteen; and the female also brooded the young for periods of 3, 2, 2 and 2 minutes. The female emerged with fæces seven times, with a dead grass-blade once; the male never emerged with fæces. On this day the male was feeding almost entirely green caterpillars which he collected from distances up to 400 yards away (near the camp). The female brought spiders and harvestmen; once there

were some green caterpillars in a beakful of these. The green caterpillars proved to be sawfly larvae. The first fledged young in the oasis were seen at the Hnífá on 12 July.

2. Meadow-Pipit (*Anthus pratensis*).—Not an uncommon breeding bird. One nest found near camp on 16 July with five fresh eggs. Fledged birds of the year first seen on 14 July.

3. Blue-headed Wagtail (*Motacilla flava*).—On 15 July, at the cold springs at Nautalda, we all saw in good light at twenty to thirty yards a wagtail with bright sulphur-yellow underparts, a greenish back and a dark slate head, with even darker cheeks. Its tail did not seem to be *particularly* long and as it fed about the springs at this place it made chirps which two of us thought very like those of *M. flava.* In flight it uttered a louder, more penetrating and slightly metallic chirp and showed white outer tail-feathers. The greenish back (among other characteristics) leads us to determine it as a member of one of the dark-headed races of *M. flava* rather than *M. cinerea*, the grey wagtail. This is a new species for Iceland, though vagrant grey wagtails have occasionally been recorded before. For our troubles with identification, see p. 91.

4. White Wagtail (*Motacilla alba*).—A few appeared on passage at the Base Camp at the end of July. One 29 July, two or three 30 July, one 1 August.

5. Wheatear (*Oenanthe oenanthe*).—Two immature birds seen near Arnarfellsbrekka on 21 July. They flew well and had, therefore, probably been hatched elsewhere. Two seen on passage, Bólstaður, end July.

6. Snowy Owl (*Nyctea scandiaca*).—An adult male seen on 17 July and probably the same bird again on 18 July. (A known breeding ground of this species is some forty miles from the oasis.)

7. Iceland Falcon (*Falco rusticolus*).—Single birds seen on many occasions and a pair seen together on 25 July. These birds were feeding on pinkfoot goslings. There was no evidence of breeding, but one or two pairs might well have been breeding not far away.

8. White-tailed Eagle (*Haliaeetus albicilla*).—A single immature with dark tail was living in the area and was frequently seen. He was remarkably tame, allowing a mounted approach to within fifty or sixty yards. Ptarmigan, goslings and possibly even an adult pinkfoot (see p. 93) are known to have been part of his diet.

9. Whooper Swan (*Cygnus cygnus*).—Discovered breeding at Arnarfellsbrekka by W. L. Watts (1876) in 1875 and Foster in 1876. On 14 August 1881 J. Coles (1882) found a flightless flock of 12 at the mouth of the Hnífá, and on 15 August another flock, of which only one could fly and at least four were cygnets, in Þúfuver. Some twenty pairs were probably breeding in the oasis in 1951, including Þúfuver. Eleven nests or broods were found there and five more were found on the journeys in and out.

The clutch sizes were as follows:

Number of eggs or cygnets	5	4	3	2	1	0
Number of nests or broods	3	3	6	2	–	1

The empty nest was attended and may have been recently predated.

The nests were large mounds of reddish moss, built among pools (but not usually on islands), which had dried up some time before hatching time. They were, therefore, in all cases easily accessible. The eggs were heavily stained reddish brown—the colour of the mud in the dried-up beds of the pools.

The behaviour of nesting whoopers was very variable. Most females left the nest as soon as the intruder came into sight. One pen crouched on the nest and did not leave it until approached to within about seventy-five yards. This was unique and occurred on 25 June, apparently at least a week before the hatching date. Two pairs of swans showed extreme shyness when a photographic hide was erected more than sixty yards from their nests. One pair deserted and in the other case the hide was only just removed in time.

On one occasion a pen left a nest as a result of hearing the alarm note of a pinkfoot, while the intruders were still out of sight over a ridge. She apparently left in a hurry as the eggs had not been covered.

The first cygnets were seen on 2 July, and most nests were hatched by 11 July although one still had eggs on 14 July.

The very pale grey (almost white) down of a whooper cygnet is stiffer than that of ducks and geese and makes the bird softer, more resilient, more velvety to the touch. The peaky bill is grey, with a patch of flesh colour near the base. The legs are quite bright orange pink.

Whooper cygnets would sometimes follow humans even when at least a week old. Newly hatched cygnets usually followed, and a hasty retreat was necessary if they were not to be led away from the nest. Older cygnets would feign death when handled, hanging their necks in a lifeless attitude. This was particularly noticed in a brood estimated to be about two weeks old, and again in one of about four and a half weeks.

One newly hatched cygnet had a kink in its neck and was totally unable to lift its head or to move from the nest. It was destroyed and the skin preserved.

The behaviour of parent whoopers with cygnets was also variable. Some deserted their brood and flew away at a range of several hundred yards. Others remained to protect their young and were photographed at less than thirty yards. A characteristic brood was found on 12 July and is described in P. S.'s diary:

"Ahead of us was another pair of swans, this time with three cygnets. Again Finnur and I went after them. The parents were very brave and stayed until we were about twenty yards away. Then they only flew fifty yards, and later another fifty. We tagged the three cygnets and let them away. They were quite young, but not a bit inclined to follow us. This may have been because the pen was only a hundred yards away and, although out of sight over the ridge, she was still calling. They ran off in her direction and as we retreated, so the pen started to come back. By the time we reached the horses, she had breasted the ridge, and suddenly saw the cygnets. She bowled down the hill at a good pace to meet them. Her first sight of them and final meeting with them were delightfully reflected in a change of note in her almost continuous calls. As she began to lead the young ones away the cob flew round and settled with them. The family was safely reunited barely two hundred yards from us. In the distance I saw a single swan flying, and presently the cob took off. I thought he was interested in the intrusion of the other swan, but he settled ahead of us as we proceeded and began to walk away. As we rode towards him he rose again and settled another few hundred yards ahead. I believe this was an attempt to lead us away. We all agreed that this family of swans had given us a great deal of sentimental pleasure. They were noble birds and they had behaved nobly. We had succeeded in marking the young and the whole operation had been performed quickly, tidily, and without risk of loss to the family. We rode on in good spirits in spite of the drizzling rain."

On 8 July a pair of swans with one cygnet swam through the territory of an arctic tern and were repeatedly attacked. The swans ducked their heads every time the tern dived.

The swan families (unlike the pinkfeet) did not form flocks and wander in the oasis, but remained separate and in the same general area as the nest. On two occasions swans were seen driving off goose families with vigour. In both cases the goose parents were counter-attacking, but the fight was too far away to assess casualties.

The first flightless swan was the female of a broodless pair seen on 22 July. The cob flew off and the pen remained on a small lake, refusing to be driven ashore. On 24 July the first flightless parent was seen (and marked). This was also a pen, with three cygnets two weeks old. The cob was still able to fly. This pen had pale blue-grey eyes (the iris is normally brown). Of a pair with four cygnets (about four weeks old) encountered on the Dalsá during the return journey on 3 August the pen was flightless but the cob was still able to fly. Besides the above only one of a broodless pair encountered on 1 August was flightless and it was thought to be the pen. Thus there is some evidence that female whooper swans (as is perhaps the case with pink-footed geese) moult before the males.

One adult female and twenty-two cygnets were marked with wing-tags.

[Grey Lag Goose (*Anser anser*).—Breeds commonly in lower Þjórsá valley (Pearson, 1895). Pairs with small young were seen on the river on 24 June, the second day of the journey in, at the junction of the Tungnaá with the Þjórsá. This is some fifty miles south of the oasis. At dawn on 26 June a flock was heard flying along the river at Kjálkaver, some twenty miles below the oasis. No single grey lag was seen during the summer on the Þjórsárver við Hofsjökul.]

10. Pink-footed Goose (*Anser brachyrhynchus*).—Probably the commonest bird in the oasis (dunlin next).

11. Barnacle Goose (*Branta leucopsis*).—A single gander was mated to a female pinkfoot which had a nest of four eggs on 29 June. The nest was later predated. (The species occurs in Iceland on passage to and from the breeding grounds in North-east Greenland.)

12. Pintail (*Anas acuta*).—A few pairs were breeding in the oasis. Two nests of fresh eggs were found close together on 28 June and four newly hatched ducklings were seen with the mother on 12 July. These were all close to the Base Camp. On 28 June two drakes and one duck were seen in the marsh where the four ducklings subsequently appeared. These were the only pintail seen.

13. Teal (*Anas crecca*).—A recently predated nest was found at

Kjálkaver, on the inward journey, on 25 June. One female was seen near Arnarfellsbrekka on 21 July. It was not thought to be breeding. Flank feathers of a drake were found at the hot springs at Nauthagi.

14. Scaup (*Aythya marila*).—No males seen. One female with seven hard set eggs on 11 July. Four ducklings with mother 22 July, which could have been from the same nest but probably were not. One other female seen on 15 July, thought to be nesting but no nest found.

15. Long-tailed Duck (*Clangula hyemalis*).—The commonest duck in the oasis, but not more than twenty to thirty seen altogether. The majority of these appeared to be non-breeders, and in plumage in which the sexes were not easy to distinguish. Five seen together on 15 July on a pool in marsh were performing low intensity display activities. All five looked at first sight like females, but one had more white about the face and was darker on the back. It is unlikely that long-tailed ducks breed in their first year. (Their near relations the eider-ducks and the goldeneyes do not do so.) Thus these birds may have been yearlings of both sexes.

No nests were found, but two broods of newly hatched young were seen on 15 July (three and seven). Another brood of three was seen on 20 July.

16. Harlequin Ducks (*Histrionicus histrionicus*).—Two females were seen on the Hnífá, on various dates in July, but there was no evidence of breeding. This river is not glacial and its water is clear. Glacier rivers such as the Þjórsá and its higher tributaries evidently do not provide a suitable habitat for this species. A pair of harlequins was seen on 25 June during the journey in, at a clear burn, the Hölkná, some thirty miles south of the oasis.

17. Great Northern Diver (*Colymbus immer*).—One seen 27 June, a pair flying up the river on 30 June. Not apparently breeding in the area.

18. Red-throated Diver (*Colymbus stellatus*).—A few pairs breeding in the oasis. Two small young on 2 July, and two more on 7 July. The only food available for miles around appeared to be sticklebacks (*Gasterosteus aculeatus*) which were found by us in the Miklakvísl, from the hot springs of Nauthagi to its mouth. No other fish occurs in the oasis as the glacier rivers are unsuitable for trout or char. For some time one diver was watched by two

of us, through powerful glasses in good light, attending its young with a small fish in its mouth which strongly resembled (but could not be proved to be) a stickleback. However, it is quite possible that the local divers fetched some of their food from lakes containing trout or char, even though the nearest are probably over twenty-five miles to the south, in the Veiðivatn area. It is well known that in other parts of Iceland red-throated divers may nest a long distance from their staple food.

One of the 7 July brood was found sitting on shore, apparently ailing. It was marked, but probably did not survive as only one young bird was in evidence on 19 July. Chick's down was dark sooty grey, to black—not " mouse-brown " as has been described. The bill, legs and eyes were black (iris being indistinguishable from pupil).

One chick was seen to dive in alarm when its mother flew down to settle on the water beside it. One adult, disturbed on a long, narrow tundra-lochan, first dived, and then flew away in the direction opposite to that of its dive, pattering for over a hundred yards before taking off down-wind.

19. WHIMBREL (*Numenius phaeopus*).—Many pairs breeding in the oasis, although no nests or young found (except young already able to fly). Behaviour of adults indicated eggs or young in vicinity on many occasions but time was not available to search for them. One nest of four eggs found at Starkaðsver (about fifty miles from the oasis) on 24 June, during the journey in.

Generally, however, the bird is not so common in the Central Highlands as it is in the farmlands of Iceland.

[SNIPE (*Capella gallinago*).—One was seen at Kjálkaver, on the inward journey on 25 June.]

20. RED-NECKED PHALAROPE (*Phalaropus lobatus*).—A few pairs were breeding. A nest with four hard set eggs was found near the Base Camp on 26 June. Not nearly so common in the Central Highlands as in other parts of Iceland. On 4 July a bird was seen in full winter plumage, in company with a female in full summer plumage. As usual with this species they were very tame and photographs were obtained of this interesting bird at ranges of ten to fifteen feet. They were seen to be feeding on the crustacean *Lepidurus*. On the same date a flock of seventeen was playing on a tundra-lochan.

21. DUNLIN (*Calidris alpina*).—Probably the second commonest bird in the oasis (pink-footed goose commonest). In spite of this

only two nests found: 27 June, four eggs; 20 July, female sitting on two bad eggs. A young bird just able to fly was seen on 21 July. Hovering song-flight was still at its height in late June but was no longer commonly heard after end of first week in July. Dunlins were seen in flocks on 4 July. Twenty-five were together on 10 July. On the inward journey we saw a large flock at Hólaskógur on 23 June.

The curious association of dunlins with other species, notably golden plovers, was frequently noted. "Plover's page" is a local name for the dunlin. A translation of the Icelandic name is "plover's slave." Golden plovers were rarely seen without dunlins in attendance. The plover apparently plays a passive part, but the relationship is evidently rather complex. Dunlins also fraternised with purple sandpipers. The most curious case was a dunlin seen on 28 June which stood regularly within six inches of an incubating arctic tern. From time to time the dunlin left to feed and preen at the water's edge, always returning to the same spot beside the nesting tern.

On 3 July a dunlin performed high-intensity injury-feigning and "rodent-run." The bird ran away crouching with white tail lowered and dark central tail-feathers forming a narrow black line (conceivably suggesting a rodent's tail). When it stopped it was always in a hollow crouching almost out of sight, as if at pains not to give a clear view of itself to the enemy. The performance was accompanied by a loud squealing noise, quite unlike any normal dunlin call note, but remarkably like the squeal of a rat.

22. Purple Sandpiper (*Calidris maritima*).—Not a common breeding bird. No eggs found but parents maintained territories; a young bird only just able to fly was seen on 21 July, a fledged brood on 28 July and a small chick on 29 July. Both parents of the last feigned injury, and one (probably the female) performed a remarkable "rodent-run," accompanied by a shrill squeal totally unrelated to any normal call-note of this species.

23. Redshank (*Tringa totanus*).—One heard at night 26 June. A flying young bird (traces of down still visible on head) seen at the warm springs at Nauthagi 29 July. The complete absence of the species from the area between these dates indicates that the young bird had been hatched elsewhere.

24. Ringed Plover (*Charadrius hiaticula*).—Rather less common than the purple sandpiper, but several pairs nesting on shingle-banks

beside braided channels of streams, or on bare gravel mounds and hillocks. No eggs found but small young seen on 22 July and 31 July. In both cases parents feigned injury; in the latter both parents took part, but female at higher intensity; the tail was spread, sharply depressed and drooped on the side towards the enemy.

25. Golden Plover (*Pluvialis apricaria*).—Only slightly less numerous than the dunlin. All present were visibly of the subspecies *altifrons*. Ubiquitous breeding species in the oasis, but no eggs or young found until flying young were seen on many occasions in late July (dates not recorded). Golden plovers standing near nests or young were frequently attended by dunlins.

On 7 July injury-feigning is described in P. S.'s diary: "At one place on the river (Hnífá) a golden plover did the best injury-feigning I have seen from this species. The bird sat looking normal in front of us, then the tail was depressed, slightly at first and then sharply down to the ground; then the wings began to droop, one more than the other. Then she flitted across the river, both legs dangling; and once on the other side she ran through the scrub in a very plausible 'rodent-run.' The male joined her and also performed the 'rodent-run.' Then the female came back and repeated the performance exactly."

26. Arctic Tern (*Sterna macrura*).—A very few pairs were breeding in the oasis. Only one nest was found, on 28 June. The eggs were collected and the bird had laid again in the same nest when the site was revisited on 15 July. The first clutch was two eggs, the second only one. A tern was seen vigorously attacking a pair of whooper swans with a cygnet on 8 July; it was evidently attempting to drive them away from the vicinity of its own eggs or young. Small numbers of terns which may have been on passage were seen hawking across the marshes in late July. On one occasion three or four terns were seen following and mobbing a tiercel Iceland falcon, which appeared completely oblivious of their presence.

27. Great Black-backed Gull (*Larus marinus*).—Commonly seen in small numbers throughout the summer but no evidence of breeding. Thirty or forty believed to be living in the oasis. This is the principal species living on the eggs and goslings of the pinkfeet.

28. Arctic Skua (*Stercorarius parasiticus*).—Probably not room for more than about ten breeding pairs in the oasis. Only two nests found, one in Illaver on 4 July with a single but well-incubated

egg and one on the Hnífá on 12 July with two eggs. Of perhaps thirty different birds seen only two were of the light phase, and one was intermediate. Typical injury-feigning was seen on several occasions. Once both birds performed immediately beyond the nest, thus leading the intruders towards it.

No direct evidence was found that the skuas were either taking pinkfoot eggs or killing goslings, although one persistently attacked a gull which was robbing a goose's nest, and another attacked a gull eating a gosling. Though not proved, it seems likely that eggs or young of geese must frequently be eaten, if not originally destroyed by the skuas. A pair was seen feeding on a gosling killed by a falcon. Two were seen chasing a dunlin.

29. Ptarmigan (*Lagopus mutus*).—A few pairs breeding in the oasis. No this-year's nests were found. By 17 July only two birds had been seen; on that date a cock performed the display flight, rising in a long glide, stalling and then parachuting down on quivering wings with loud crowing. The first brood was seen on 21 July on the terminal moraine of the glacier, Arnarfellsmúlar. Five of the young were wing-tagged, two being recovered later in the summer by members of the British Schools Exploring Society's Expedition. A brood already capable of flight (although the young were, of course, still quite small) was seen at Eyvafen on 26 July, and another brood of eleven with both parents in attendance was seen in Tjarnarver on 29 July.

APPENDIX D

LIST OF PLANTS
(*PTERIDOPHYTA AND SPERMATOPHYTA*)
Found in the Þjórsárver við Hofsjökul (north of Fjórdungssandur), 1951

by Finnur Guðmundsson

(*Reprinted from the Fifth Annual Report of the Severn Wildfowl Trust*)

I. *PTERIDOPHYTA*

Ophioglossaceae

1. *Ophioglossum vulgatum* L. var. *polyphyllum* A. Br.
2. *Botrychium lunaria* (L.) Sw.

Equisetaceae

3. *Equisetum arvense* L.

Selaginellaceae

4. *Selaginella selaginoides* (L.) Lk.

II. *SPERMATOPHYTA*

Potamogetonaceae

5. *Potamogeton alpinus* Balvis.

Gramineae

6. *Phleum commutatum* Gaud.
7. *Agrostis stolonifera* L.
8. *Calamagrostis neglecta* (Ehrh.) G., M. & Sch.
9. *Deschampsia alpina* (L.) R. & Sch.
10. *Trisetum spicatum* (L.) P. Richter.
11. *Poa glauca* Vahl.
12. „ *alpina* L.
13. *Festuca rubra* L.
14. „ *vivipara* (L.) Sm.

Cyperaceae

15. *Eriophorum Scheuchzeri* Hoppe.
16. *Eriophorum angustifolium* Honck.
17. *Kobresia myosuroides* (Vill.) F. & Paol.
18. *Carex canescens* L.
19. „ *Lachenalii* Schkuhr.
20. „ *rariflora* (Wg.) Sm.
21. „ *rostrata* Stokes.
22. „ *saxatilis* L.
23. „ *Goodenoughii* Gay.
24. „ *Lyngbyei* Hornem.
25. „ *rigida* Good.

Juncaceae

26. *Juncus arcticus* Willd.
27. „ *biglumis* L.
28. „ *articulatus* L.
29. *Luzula spicata* (L.) D. C.
30. „ *arcuata* (Wg.) Sw.

Liliaceae

31. *Tofieldia pusilla* (Michx.) Pers.

Orchidaceae

32. *Coeloglossum viride* (L.) Hartm.

Salicaceae

33. *Salix glauca* L.
34. „ *lanata* L.
35. „ *herbacea* L.
36. „ *phylicifolia* L.

Betulaceae

37. *Betula nana* L.

Polygonaceae

38. *Rumex Acetosa* L.
39. *Oxyria digyna* (L.) Hill.
40. *Koenigia islandica* L.
41. *Polygonum viviparum* L.

Caryophyllaceae

42. *Stellaria crassifolia* Ehrh.
43. *Cerastium cerastoides* (L.) Britton.
44. „ *alpinum* L.
45. *Sagina intermedia* Fenzl.
46. *Minuartia rubella* (Wg.) Hiern.
47. „ *biflora* (L.) Schinz & Thell.
48. *Arenaria norvegica* Gunn.
49. *Viscaria alpina* (L.) Don.
50. *Silene maritima* With.
51. „ *acaulis* (L.) Jacq.

Ranunculaceae

52. *Ranunculus acris* L.
53. „ *pygmaeus* Wg.
54. „ *reptans* L.
55. *Thalictrum alpinum* L.

Cruciferae

56. *Draba rupestris* R. Br.
57. *Cardamine pratensis* L.
58. „ *bellidifolia* L.
59. *Arabis alpina* L.
60. *Cardaminopsis petraea* (L.) Hiit.

Crassulaceae

61. *Sedum vittosum* L.
62. „ *roseum* (L.) Scop.

Saxifragaceae

63. *Saxifraga caespitosa* L.
64. „ *hypnoides boreali-atlantica* Engl. & Irmsch.
65. „ *cernua* L.
66. „ *rivularis* L.
67. „ *oppositifolia* L.
68. „ *hirculus* L.
69. „ *nivalis* L.
70. „ *tenuis* (Wg.) H. Sm.
71. „ *stellaris* L.
72. *Parnassia palustris* L.

Rosaceae

73. *Sibbaldia procumbens* L.
74. *Comarum palustre* L.
75. *Potentilla Crantzii* (Cr.) G. Beck.
76. *Dryas octopetala* L.
77. *Alchemilla glomerulans* Bus.

Geraniaceae

78. *Geranium silvaticum* L.

Violaceae

79. *Viola palustris* L.

Onagraceae

80. *Chamaenerion latifolium* (L.) Sweet.
81. *Epilobium palustre* L.
82. „ *anagallidifolium* Lam.
83. „ *lactiflorum* Hausskn.

Hippuridaceae

84. *Hippuris vulgaris* L.

Umbelliferae

85. *Archangelica officinalis* Hoffm.

Pyrolaceae

86. *Pyrola minor* L.

Ericaceae

87. *Cassiope hypnoides* (L.) Don.
88. *Vaccinium uliginosum* L.

Empetraceae

89. *Empetrum nigrum* L.

Plumbaginaceae

90. *Armeria vulgaris* Willd.

Gentianaceae

91. *Gentiana tenella* Rottb.
92. „ *nivalis* L.
93. *Menyanthes trifoliata* L.

Labiatae

94. *Thymus arcticus* (Dur.) Ronn.

Scrophulariaceae

95. *Rhinanthus minor* L.
96. *Bartsia alpina* L.
97. *Euphrasia* sp.

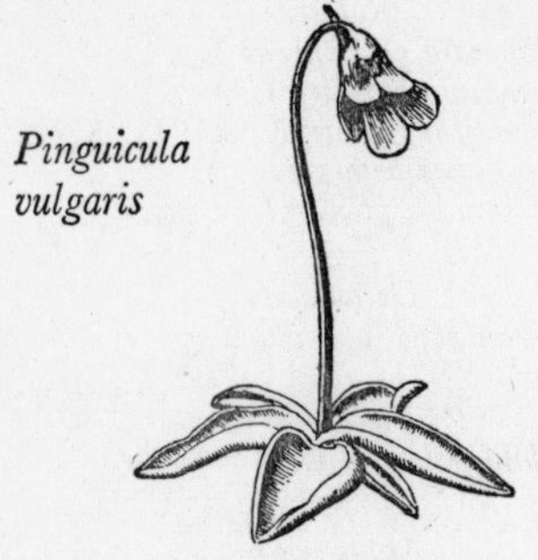
Pinguicula vulgaris

98. *Pedicularis flammea* L.
99. *Veronica fruticans* Jacq.
100. „ *alpina* L.

Lentibulariaceae

101. *Pinguicula vulgaris* L.

Rubiaceae

102. *Galium pumilum* (L.) Murr.

Compositae

103. *Erigeron boreale* (Vierh.) Simm.
104. „ *uniflorum* L.
105. *Gnaphalium supinum* L.
106. *Taraxacum* sp.
107. *Hieracium alpinum* (L.) Backh.
108. „ *percome* Om.

Systematic arrangement after Stefán Stefánsson's *Flóra Íslands* (1948 ed.).

Several of the above plants had a very restricted distribution. Thus the following species were only found at the hot springs of Nauthagi: *Ophioglossum vulgatum*, *Potamogeton alpinus*, *Agrostis stolonifera*, *Carex canescens*, *Stellaria crassifolia*, *Ranunculus reptans*, *Comarum palustre*, *Menyanthes trifoliata*, *Rhinanthus minor*.

Juncus articulatus was only found at the hot springs in Jökulkriki.

Cardamine bellidifolia was only found on Ólafsfell. The tiny *Draba* specimens found on Ólafsfell proved on examination to be a variety of *Draba rupestris*, which by some authors is thought to be a distinct species (*Draba norvegica*).

The following is a complete list of the species growing on the roof and in the walls of the *kofi* or hut of stone and turf near the Base Camp at Bólstaður. There was a hatched pinkfoot's nest on the roof of this *kofi*. The vegetation is therefore typical of a pinkfoot nesting site.

1. *Poa glauca.*
2. „ *alpina.*
3. *Festuca rubra.*
4. *Carex rigida.*
5. *Luzula spicata.*
6. *Salix glauca.*
7. „ *lanata.*
8. „ *herbacea.*
9. *Rumex acetosa.*
10. *Polygonum viviparum.*
11. *Cerastium alpinum.*
12. *Sagina intermedia.*
13. *Minuartia rubella.*
14. *Silene acaulis.*
15. *Thalictrum alpinum.*
16. *Draba rupestris.*
17. *Cardaminopsis petraea.*
18. *Saxifraga caespitosa.*
19. „ *oppositifolia.*
20. *Potentilla Crantzii.*
21. *Chamaenerion latifolium.*
22. *Armeria vulgaris.*
23. *Thymus arcticus.*
24. *Galium pumilum.*
25. *Taraxacum* sp.

APPENDIX E

THE PROBABLE PINKFOOT POPULATION OF THE ÞJÓRSÁRVER VID HOFSJÖKUL IN 1951

(*Reprinted from the Fifth Annual Report of the Severn Wildfowl Trust*)

The collaboration of Hugh Boyd is gratefully acknowledged

Size of the Breeding Colony

Although by all calculations there must have been many thousands of geese within the thirteen-mile square which encompassed the breeding grounds, one of the most striking features of the summer was that so few of them were in evidence. For example on 28 June, two days after the expedition's arrival, seventy-four geese were counted in the air, and this was very much the largest flock we had then seen. On the following day a hundred were estimated in Falcon Marsh. On 4 July the whole face of Arnarfellsalda appeared to be covered with geese, yet, when counted, there were only ninety adults with their goslings in an estimated square mile. Only once was a really large number of geese to be seen. From the top of Arnarfellsalda on a very clear day at least five hundred adults with goslings were spread out across the flat marsh to the north.

Otherwise, by far the largest assemblies of geese were those resulting from our drives, which nearly always brought in more than we expected.

Two methods of estimating the population were available:

(1) Counts of nests found in measured areas, from which the total number of nests in the oasis could be calculated.

(2) The number of birds already marked which were recaptured in subsequent catches could provide estimates of the population of both adults and goslings.

1. Nest-Counts.—The total area of the biotope was found to be 114 sq. km. (44 sq. miles), of which 82 sq. km. was explored, 32 sq. km. remaining unvisited. In transects totalling 102 km. in

length sixty-seven nests were found. It was not possible to maintain a constant width of transect-strip but the mean width was about 20 m., so that the area searched was $102 \times \frac{20}{1000} = 2{\cdot}04$ sq. km. with a nest density of 33 nests per sq. km. (84 per sq. mile). If this density was typical the number of nests in the whole area was 33×114, or about 3,700. But this is almost certainly too high since much of the area was bog and tundra pools which could not be transected (or colonised).

More intensive search of a small area showed that the nests were not distributed uniformly or randomly even over apparently suitable terrain but occurred in groups. In view of this discontinuous distribution it was considered that the mean density of nests might be of the order of fifteen nests per square kilometre rather than the higher figure indicated by the transects. This would make the number of nests in the colony about 1,700. It would require much more extensive sampling to obtain an accurate estimate of the size of the breeding population by this method.

2. Recaptures.—1,151 geese were marked (382 adults and 769 goslings). Sixty-two birds marked from 28 June onwards were recaptured on or before 1 August (seven adults and fifty-five goslings; one gosling recaptured twice). The two geese ringed in Britain and recaptured on 25 July have no bearing on this estimate of population and are not included as "recaptures" in these calculations.

Estimation of the size of a population (T) from the recapture of previously marked birds (x) in a catch of n individuals is based on the ratio $T : m :: n : x$ or $T = \frac{m.n}{x}$ where m is the number of birds marked and released prior to the day of sampling. This index has been used in estimating populations of many kinds of animals. Ricker (1948) in a review of its applications has listed six conditions which must be complied with if its use is to be valid.

1. The natural mortality of marked and unmarked animals must be the same.
2. Marked animals must not lose their marks.
3. All marked animals must be recognised on recapture.
4. The amount of recruitment to the population being sampled during the sampling period must be negligible.
5. Marked animals must be as subject to sampling as unmarked ones.

6. The marked animals must become randomly mixed with the unmarked ones, *or*, the distribution of sampling effort must be proportional to the number of animals in different parts of the habitat being studied.

The first four requirements are thought to have been satisfied in this problem. Because the technique of capture involved driving the geese to the trap, condition 5 was probably not satisfied. There is some evidence that previously caught geese show " trap-shyness." This probably affects adults more than goslings and, since they are in any case less easy to catch than young birds, has made it desirable to use separate estimates of the numbers of adults and goslings.

The mixing of marked and unmarked geese was not random, first, because geese remain in family parties and in larger aggregates (though these are much less stable than families) rather than disperse individually, and second, because the intervals of time between successive catches were of necessity so short that the amount of intermingling possible could not have resulted in randomness. Some effects of these limitations are shown in the table of estimates and the notes which follow. But, since catches were made in many parts of the habitat and roughly in proportion to the numbers of geese in those parts, the application of the index should provide useful estimates of the total population, though the standard of accuracy attainable is not high.

Recently Bailey (1951, 1952) has shown that $m.\left(\frac{n+1}{x+1}\right)$ provides a better estimate of the population size than $m.\frac{n}{x}$ and this modified form of the index has been used but, in view of the limitations of accuracy just noted, it has seemed inappropriate to employ the measures of variance suggested by him.

The five large catches made by driving the geese into nets may each be used to give a population estimate (Table A). The results are widely different (adults 2,020-10,580, goslings 1,930-18,330). Some of the reasons for the lack of agreement are apparent. Two of the catches (Oddkelsalda 28 July, Arnarfellsalda 31 July) were made at sites where geese had been caught only three days before. It is evident that the much higher proportions of recaptures obtained in these two catches are due to the continued presence in the vicinity of birds taken in the earlier catches. The resulting enhanced values of x reduce the values of T, very obviously in the gosling estimates and rather less strikingly in the adult estimates, and these two sets of results therefore provide estimates of total population which are almost certainly much too low. The totals given by the catch of 1 August are, by contrast, probably too high because the birds sampled were more or less isolated from the sites of earlier marking operations by the presence between them of the Base Camp. Thus the number of marked birds available for recapture in the Round-up Hill area was probably artificially reduced, so that the values of x are small, giving very large values of T.

Another source of weakness in the calculations is the small total number of recaptures, particularly of adults. In general large values of m, n and x lead to more accurate estimates of T than small ones. For this reason, in the second set of three estimates, we have had recourse to grouping, and this has the additional advantage of combining catches in which the proportion of recaptures is known to be too high with one in which it is likely to have been too low. Thus these two sources of error may minimise, though they are unlikely to eliminate, each other.

Even when the catches are grouped the three sets of estimates are not in close agreement, but the mean values are thought to be the best estimates of the size of the population that can be obtained from the recapture data.

Relative Numbers of Adults and Goslings

The ratio of adults : goslings in the various catches do not represent the true proportion in the population, because of the greater unwillingness of adults to be driven into nets. The only catch in which the ratio is thought likely to resemble the true one is that of 1 August, when a large measure of surprise was achieved, so that the adults had less opportunity to escape. The adult : gosling ratio in this catch was 85 : 120. This may be used to give additional estimates of the total numbers of each class, as in Table B.

The proportion of non-breeding adults present is not known, though evidence of their presence is provided by one of the recaptures of British-ringed birds, since this bird was less than one year old when ringed in the autumn of 1950 and so could not have been sexually mature in the summer of 1951.

Appendix E

TABLE A

Estimates of the Pinkfoot Population at Þjórsárver við Hofsjökul from Recapture of Marked Geese

Dates and sites of Catches used for sampling	Adults				Goslings			
	Number Marked Previously m	Number Captured n	Number of Marked Adults Recaptured x	Estimated Total of Adults in oasis $T_a = m.\left(\frac{n+1}{x+1}\right)$	Number Marked Previously m	Number Captured n	Number of Marked Goslings Recaptured x	Estimated Total of Goslings in Oasis $Tg = m.\left(\frac{n+1}{x+1}\right)$
25 July, Oddkelsalda ..	76	98	2	2,510	269	165	4	8,930
28 July, Oddkelsalda ..	174	23	1	2,090	438	74	16	1,930
28 July, Arnarfellsalda ..	174	55	2	3,250	438	125	4	11,040
31 July, Arnarfellsalda ..	252	15	1	2,020	616	99	23	2,570
1 August, Round-up Hill ..	252	83	1	10,580	616	118	3	18,330
25 July and later ..	76	276	3	5,260	269	583	15	9,820
28 July and later ..	174	178	4	6,230	438	418	28	6,330
31 July and 1 August	252	98	2	8,320	616	217	26	4,970
				mean 6,660				*mean* 7,040

Notes.—1. It may safely be assumed that none of the birds captured on Oddkelsalda on 28 July could have reached Arnarfellsalda by the time of the second catch on that day, and, similarly, that birds captured on 31 July at Arnarfellsalda could not have reached Round-up Hill by the following morning.

2. The recaptures used here are only those marked *before* the first recapture date given, e.g. the fifteen marked birds recaptured on and after 25 July were all marked before 25 July.

3. The mean values are obtained from the three totals based on the grouped catches (below the line), excluding the totals based on single catches.

TABLE B

SIZE OF BREEDING COLONY OF PINK-FOOTED GEESE AT ÞJÓRSÁRVER VIÐ HOFSJÖKUL IN 1951

Method of Estimation	Nests	Adults	Goslings	Total	Remarks
1. Nest-count by transects	3,700	8,400 [1]	11,900	20,300	*Too high because of uncolonised bog and water*
2. Nest-count by area density	1,700	4,400 [1]	6,200	10,600	—
3. Recaptures	—	6,700	7,000	13,700	*Goslings too low due to inadequate mixing. Adults too high because of trap-shyness*
4. Recaptures of adults and $\frac{\text{adult}}{\text{gosling}}$ ratio for goslings	—	6,600	9,300	15,900	—
5. Recaptures of goslings and $\frac{\text{adult}}{\text{gosling}}$ ratio for adults	—	5,000	7,000	12,000	*More accurate than 4 because of more gosling recaptures than adult recaptures*
6. Estimate based on assessment of value of various methods ..	2,300	5,500	7,500	13,000[2]	

[1] An arbitrary figure of 1,000 is added as non-breeding adults are not otherwise accounted for.

[2] The discoveries of the Trust's 1953 expedition to the oasis, though they have not yet been fully worked out, seem, at least at first sight, to confirm these estimates.

APPENDIX F

BIBLIOGRAPHY

This is mainly confined to literature seen during the preparation of this book and the various reports of the expedition, which throws light on the breeding *distribution and habits of the pinkfoot.*

BAILEY, N. T. J. (1951). On estimating the size of mobile populations from recapture data. *Biometrika*, *38*: 293 (1952). Improvements in the interpretation of recapture data. *J. Anim. Ecol.*, *21*: 120-27.

BARING-GOULD, S. (1863). *Iceland, its scenes and sagas.* London.

BAY, E. (1894). Den østgrønlandske Expedition udfort i Aarene 1891–92 under Ledelse af C. Ryder. I. Hvirveldyr. *Medd. Grønland*, *19*: no. 1; 51 pp. (32-33).

BENT, A. C. (1925). Life histories of North American wildfowl, . . . Part 2. *Bull. U.S. Nat. Mus.*, No. 130; 200-04.

BERTRAM, G. C. L., LACK, D. and ROBERTS, B. B. (1934). Notes on East Greenland birds. . . . *Ibis* (13), *4*: 816-31 (819).

BIRD, C. G. and BIRD, E. G. (1941). The birds of North-East Greenland. *Ibis* (14), *5*: 116-61 (121-23, 133-34).

BIRD, E. G. (1934). Notes on the geese, etc., of Iceland. *Ibis* (13), *4*: 170.

BJÖRNSSON, M. (1932–34). Nokkur orð um grágæsir og helsingja. *Náttúrufræðingurinn Reykjavik*, *2*: 143-52; *3*: 17-22, 75-78, 129-32; *4*: 30-40, 166-75.

BONAR, H. N. (1901). A list of the birds of Spitsbergen. . . . *Trans. Scot. Nat. Hist. Soc.*, *1*: 249-61 (250).

BRUCE, W. S. (1908). The exploration of Prince Charles Foreland, 1906–1907. *Geogr. J.*, *32*: 139-48.

CHAPMAN, A. (1889). A voyage to Spitzbergen and the Arctic seas. *Nat. Hist. Trans. N'humb.*, *8*: 138-50. (1897.) *Wild Norway, with chapters on Spitsbergen, Denmark, etc.* London and New York.

CHAPMAN, F. S. (1932). Some field-notes on the birds of East Greenland. *Geogr. J.*, *79*: 493-96.

CLARKE, W. E. (1899). An epitome of Dr. Walter's ornithological results of a voyage to East Spitsbergen in the year 1889. *Ibis* (7), *5*: 42-51 (44).

CLAVERING, D. C. (1830). Journal of a voyage to Spitsbergen and the east coast of Greenland in H.M.S. *Griper*. *Edin. New Philos. J.*, *9*: 1-30.

COBURN, F. (1901). Brief notes on an expedition to the north of Iceland in 1899. *Zoologist* (4), *5*: 401-19 (408-09).

COCKS, A. H. (1882). Notes of a naturalist on the west coast of Spitzbergen. *Zoologist* (3), *6*: 321-32, 378-86, 404-18. (1883.) An autumn visit to Spitzbergen. *Zoologist* (3), *7*: 393-409, 433-48, 479-88.

COLES, J. (1882). *Summer travelling in Iceland*; . . . London, pp. 53-54, 56.

CONGREVE, W. M. (1929). Breeding of the Pink-footed Goose in Iceland. *Auk*, *46*: 533-34. (1929b.) The Pink-footed Goose (*Anser brachyrhynchus*) nesting in Iceland. *Bull. Brit. Ool. Assoc.*, *2*: 128-31. (1943.) Obituary. Major Sydney William Patrick Freme. *Ibis*, *85*: 522-23.

— and FREME, S. W. P. (1930). Seven weeks in eastern and northern Iceland. *Ibis* (12), *6*: 193-228.

CONWAY, W. M. (1897). *The first crossing of Spitsbergen* . . . London.

COTTAM, C. and KNAPPEN, P. (1939). Food of some uncommon North American birds. *Auk*, *56*: 138-69.

DALGETY, C. T. (1928). The birds of Edge Island. *Geogr. J.*, *72*: 139-40.

— MCNEILE, J. H. and INGRAM, M. J. (1931). Notes on birds observed in Spitsbergen during the spring of 1930. *Ibis* (13), *1*: 243-55 (246).

DEGERBØL, M. (1937). A contribution to the investigation of the fauna of the Blosseville Coast, East Greenland, . . . *Medd. Grønland*, *104*: no. 19; 16, 29.

— and MØHL-HANSEN, U. (1935). The Scoresby Sound Committee's second East Greenland expedition, . . . *Medd. Grønland*, *104*: No. 18; 10.

DEICHMANN, H. (1904). Birds of East Greenland, . . . *Medd. Grønland*, *29*: 141-56 (144-45).

EVANS, E. and STURGE, W. (1859). Notes on the birds of western Spitsbergen, as observed in 1855. *Ibis*, *1*: 166-74.

FABER, F. (1822). *Prodromus der isländischen Ornithologie.* Copenhagen. (1826). *Über das Leben der hochnordischen Vögel.* Leipzig.

FEILDEN, H. W. (1895). A flying visit to Spitsbergen. *Zoologist* (3), *19*: 81-90 (86-88).

FOSTER, C. LE N. (1879). *Across the Bursting-Sand in 1876*, ch. xi, pp. 263-81 of C. G. W. Lock, *q.v.*

FREME, S. W. P. (1930). Notes on an ornithological trip to North Iceland. *Northw. Nat.*, *5*: 8-12.

GEODÆTISK INSTITUT (1945). *Uppdráttur Íslands.* Series of 1 : 100,000 maps of Iceland.

GORDON, S. (1922). *Amid snowy wastes.* . . . London, etc., Cassell.

GUÐMUNDSSON, F. (1952). Bird protection in Iceland. *Bull. Int. Cttee. Bird Prot.*, *6*: 153-60.

HACHISUKA, M. U. (1927). *A Handbook of the Birds of Iceland.* London, Taylor and Francis.

HANTZSCH, B. (1905). *Beitrag zur Kenntnis der Vogelwelt Islands.* Berlin, Friedländer.

HELMS, O. (1926). The birds of Angmagsalik, . . . *Medd. Grønland*, *58*: 205-75 (230-31).

VON HEUGLIN, M. T. (1871). Die Vogel-Fauna im hohen Norden. *J. Orn.*, *19*: 81-107.

JOURDAIN, F. C. R. (1921). *Bull. Brit. Orn. Cl.*, *42*: 27-28. (1922). The birds of Spitsbergen and Bear Island. *Ibis* (11), *4*: 159-79 (164). (1925) in A. C. Bent, *q.v.* (201-02).

KOCH, J. P. (1912). Den Danske Ekspedition til Dronning Louises Land og tværs over Nordgrønlands Inlandsis, 1912–1913. *Geogr. Tidsskr. Kjobenhavn*, *21*: 165-91, 257-64 (259).

KOCH, L. (1930). The Danish Expedition to East Greenland in 1929. *Medd. Grønland*, *74*: 173-205 (185).

KOENIG, A. (1908). *J. Orn.*, *56*: 123-39. (1911). *Avifauna Spitzbergensis.* . . . Bonn.

KOLDEWEY, K. (1874). *The German Arctic expedition of 1869–70*, . . . London, 541.

LOCK, C. G. W. (1879). *The home of the eddas.* London.

LONGSTAFF, T. [G.] (1950). *This my voyage.* London, Murray, 253.

LØPPENTHIN, B. (1932). Die Vögel Nordostgrönlands, . . . *Medd. Grønland*, *91*: No. 6; 25, 33-38, 120.

MALMGREN, A. J. (1863). Anteckningar til Spetsbergens Fogelfauna. *Ofv. VetenskAkad. Förh.*, *20*: 87-126; and *J. Orn.*, *11*: 358-87, 447-58 (378). (1865). Nya anteckningar til Spetsbergens Fogelfauna. *Ofv. VetenskAkad. Förh.*, *21*: 377-412; and *J. Orn.*, *13*: 192-216, 261-70 (210-13).

MONTAGUE, F. A. (1926). Further notes from Spitsbergen. *Ibis* (12), *2*: 136-51 (139).

NATHORST, A. G. (1899). Kong Karls Land. *Ymer Stockholm, 19*: 1-32. (1900). *Två Somrar i Norra Ishafvet.* Stockholm, Beijers, 2 vols.

NEWTON, A. (1863). *Notes on the ornithology of Iceland*, Appendix A, pp. 399-421, of S. Baring-Gould, *q.v.* (414). (1864). On above. *Ibis, 6*: 131-33. (1865). Notes on the birds of Spitsbergen. *Ibis* (2), *1*: 199-219, 496-525. (1907). *Ootheca Wolleyana*: . . . London, Porter, 522-24.

NUNN, J. L. (1934). Pink-footed Geese in Wexford. *Brit. Birds, 27*: 306.

ODDSSON, G. (1917). De Mirabilibus Islandiæ. *Islandica, 10.*

VAN OORDT, G. J. (1921). Ornithological notes from Spitsbergen, . . . *Ardea, 10*: 129-70 (139).

PEARSON, H. J. and PEARSON, C. E. (1895). On birds observed in Iceland in 1894, with a list of the species hitherto recorded therefrom. *Ibis* (7), *1*: 237-49 (243).

PEDERSEN, A. (1926). Beiträge zur Kenntnis der Säugetier- und Vögelfauna der Ostküste Grönlands. *Medd. Grønland, 68*: 148-249 (207, 216-18). (1930). Fortgesetzte *idem. Medd. Grønland*, 77: 341-507 (425, 437-43). (1934) . . . Die Ornis des mittleren Teiles der Nordostküste Grönlands. *Medd. Grønland, 100*: No. 11; 14-15, 32. (1942). Dansk Nordsgrønlands Expedition, 1938-39. Säugetiere und Vögel. *Medd. Grønland, 128*: 1-119 (58-60).

PIKE, A. (1897). *A winter in the eightieth degree* (*Spitzbergen*), in A. Chapman, *q.v.*, 343-51 (343-44, 349).

PLESKE, T. (1928). Birds of the Eurasian tundra. *Mem. Boston. Soc. Nat. Hist., 6*: 109-484 (313).

RICKER, W. E. (1948). *Methods of estimating vital statistics of fish populations.* Indiana University Publication, Science Series No. 15.

ROBERTS, B. [B.] (1934). Notes on the birds of Central and South-east Iceland, with special reference to food-habits. *Ibis* (13), *4*: 239-64 (249-50).

LE ROI, O. (1911). Die Avifauna der Bären-Insel und des Spitzbergen-Archipelago. *Spezieller Tiel* in A. Koenig, *q.v.*

RÖMER, F. and SCHAUDINN, F. (1904). *Fauna arctica.* Jena, Fischer, vol. *4*.

SÆMUNDSSON, B. (1936). *Islensk Dýr*, III. *Fuglarnir* (*Aves Islandiæ*). Reykjavík, pp. 608-11.

SALOMONSEN, F. (1950). *Grønlands Fugle.* København, Munksgaard, part 1; 49-53.

SCHAANNING, H. T. L. (1933). A contribution to the bird-fauna of East Greenland. *Skr. Svalbard og Ishavet,* No. 49; 6-7.

SCHALOW, H. (1899). Einige Bemerkungen zur Vogelfauna von Spitzbergen. *J. Orn., 47*: 375-86 (385). (1904). *Die Vögel der Arktis,* in Römer and Schaudinn, *q.v. 4*: 79-288 (176-77). (1911). *Verh. V. Int. Orn.-Kongr. Berlin, 1910*: 77-78.

SCORESBY, W., Jr. (1823). *Journal of a voyage to the northern whale fishery*; . . . Edinburgh.

SCOTT, P. and FISHER, J. (1952). Pink-footed Geese in Iceland. *Geogr. Mag., 24*: 606-15.

— and GUÐMUNDSSON, F. (1935). The Severn Wildfowl Trust Expedition to Central Iceland 1951. *Fifth Annual Report, Severn Wildfowl Trust 1951-2*: 79-115.

SHEPHERD, C. W. (1867). *The North-west Peninsula of Iceland: being the journal of a tour in Iceland in the spring and summer of 1862.* London, pp. 140-41.

SLATER, H. H. (1901). *Manual of the birds of Iceland.* Edinburgh, David Douglas, pp. 40-44.

SUMMERHAYES, V. S. and ELTON, C. S. (1923). Contributions to the ecology of Spitsbergen and Bear Island. *J. Ecol., 11*: 214-86 (237). (1928). Further contributions to the ecology of Spitsbergen. *J. Ecol., 16*: 193-268 (208, 218, 243).

THIENEMANN, F. A. L., BREHM, L. and THIENEMANN, G. A. W. (1838). *Systematische Darstellung der Fortpflanzung der Vögel Europa's mit Abbildung der Eier.* Leipzig, part 5; 28.

THOMSON, A. L. and LEACH, E. P. (1952). Report on bird-ringing for 1951. *Brit. Birds, 45*: 265-77, 341-57 (277).

TIEDEMANN, M. (1943). Ornithologische Beobachtungen aus dem Hornsund-Gebeit auf Westspitzbergen. *J. Orn., 91*: 239-67 (242).

TIMMERMANN, G. (1933). Die Kurzschnabelgans in Island. *J. Orn., 81*: 322-30. (1938–49). Die Vögel Islands. *Visind. Ísland,* no. 21; 1-110: 24; 111-238: 28; 239-524 (1949, 355-58).

TREVOR-BATTYE, A. (1897). The birds of Spitsbergen, . . . *Ibis* (7), *3*: 574-600 (575, 580-82).

WALTER, A. (1890). Ornithologische Ergebnisse der von der Bremer geographischen Gesellschaft im Jahre 1889 veranstalteten Reise nach Ostspitzbergen. *J. Orn., 38*: 233-55 (243, 252, 254), see W. E. Clarke (1899).

WATTS, W. L. (1876). *Across the Vatna Jokull; or, scenes in Iceland; being a description of hitherto unknown regions.* London, p. 157.

WINGE, H. (1898). Grønlands Fugle. *Medd. Grønland, 21*: part 1; 1-316 (115-16).

WITHERBY, H. F. and LEACH, E. P. (1933). Movements of ringed birds from abroad to the British Isles and from the British Isles abroad. Addenda II. *Brit. Birds, 26*: 352-61 (356).

ZEDLITZ, O. (1911). Ornithologische Notizen von der " Zeppelin-Studienfahrt ", Spitzbergen, Sommer 1910. *J. Orn., 59*: 300-327 (319-20).

ÞÓRARINSSON, S., in A. ROUSSELL and others (1943). *Forntida Gardar i Island. Meddelanden fran den Nordiska Arkeologiska Undersökningen i Island Sommaren 1939*. København, Munksgaard, pp. 313-16.

INDEX

(*References to plates in heavy type*)

Part A: Species of Vertebrates in a Systematic Order

FISH

MAMMALS

BIRDS

The arrangement in Appendix C is that of Witherby's Check-List (*1941*). *This Appendix was first published before the appearance of the entirely different arrangement of the British Ornithologists' Union's* Check-List (*1952*) *which, like that of the American Ornithologists' Union, follows the classification of Wetmore, and which is followed in this Index. B.O.U.* Check-List *numbers are given.*

Index

Part B : Places

The localities in Spitsbergen and Greenland detailed in Appendices A and B, pp. 190-205, are not indexed here.

Index

Part C: People and Organisations

For convenience, most Icelanders are indexed under their patronymic, though this would not be their own practice.

Index